Locomotive Traction
2019

Pip Dunn

abc
Crécy

Crécy.co.uk

First published by Crécy Publishing Limited
2018

© Text: Pip Dunn
© Photographs: as credited

A CIP record for this book is available from the British Library

ISBN 9781910809549

Front Cover Top: Direct Rail Services' 68002 Intrepid leads 68026 on 6K41, the 1458 Valley-Crewe, nuclear flask train, past Llanfairyneubwll just a few miles into its journey on April 20 2018. The latter loco has since lost its plain DRS blue livery for Transpennine Express colours. *Anthony Hicks*

Bottom: On hire to GB Railfreight, 20189/205 lead 1Z24, the 1700 Dungeness-Victoria return leg of Pathfinder Tours' 'Diamond Twenties' charter past Snargate, near Appledoreon the Dungeness branch, on May 5 2018. *Anthony Hicks*

Rear main:
On 27 August 2018, D213 *Andania* made its return main line charter train work hauling 1Z40, the 0915 Crewe-Carlisle special. It passes Garsdale on the Settle and Carlisle line. *Anthony Hicks*

Rear below from left:
One of five DB Cargo Class 67s painted in the company's corporate livery, 67015 works Arriva Trains Wales' 1D34, the 0950 Manchester Piccadilly-Holyhead, past Penmaenmawr on 19 April 2018. *Anthony Hicks*

While on hire to Dutch operator ACTS, 5811 (ex-58039) stands at Amersfoort Pon on a charter from Rotterdam to Arnhem on 21 June 2008. This loco and its two ACTS compatriots later moved for work in France but are currently withdrawn in that country pending disposal or reuse. *Pip Dunn*

Sole surviving Class 17 Clayton D8568 approaches Thame Junction on 9 April 2017 with the 1100 from Chinnor. *Martin Loader*

Printed in Turkey by Olas Solutions

abc is an imprint of
Crécy Publishing Limited
1a Ringway Trading Estate
Shadowmoss Road
Manchester M22 5LH

www.crecy.co.uk

Contents

Introduction

Welcome to the second edition of Crecy's Locomotive Traction book. This book lists all the diesel and electric locos that have run on the UK's National rail network, either in the past under British Rail or currently through train operating companies. By listing everything, even if the vehicle is no longer with us, you can still 'tick it off' or underline it should you so desire.

There are a lot of grey areas in how we classify a loco's status and often the lines are blurred. However I have tried, as best as I can, to draw up distinct areas and therefore this book is split into four sections. They are:

Section 1 lists all the diesel and electric locomotives that are registered to run on the National Network Rail system, as well as those locos that are in store or withdrawn but owned or operated by franchised or Open Access Train Operating Companies. Even here there are some anomalies, mainly on shunting locos that may, or may not, be allowed out of the confines of the depots or yards that they work at. Locos owned by spot hire companies and third parties, but used by franchised TOCs/FOCs, are listed here.

On 16 August 2018, West Coast Railways' 57601 passes Lazonby & Kirkoswald on the Settle to Carlisle line, on the rear of the 0540 Southport-Edinburgh charter, hauled by 47746. This Class 57 has since been repainted into Northern Belle livery and named *Windsor Castle. Chris Fudge*

These locos will have details of the key detail differences that affect the work they can undertake. Also listed is their TOPS Sector code as of 8 September 2018, their livery, owner and name if appropriate. Old numbers – pre-1973 D/E numbers and all previous TOPS numbers – are also listed.

Locos owned by preservation groups that are main line registered are listed in this section. Some locos may – presently – not be fully main line compliant (such as missing GSM-R) or be a shunting locomotive without TPWS, but if they are used by a TOC then they are listed in this section. Not all locos in section 1 and 2 are on TOPS and have a pool code.

Section 2 lists all locos that are owned by spot hire companies but not main line registered or not on hire to FOCs/TOCs. These may be in industrial use or have been redeployed/sold for use abroad, and again relevant details are included. While these locos do not have current full main line registration, that could change.

Also included in this section are locos that have restricted NR registration – such as 25278, which can run between Middlesbrough and Whitby only.

It also details all ex-BR and ex-TOC/FOC locomotives that have been sold for private use or pending disposal. Also included in this section are any locos that have been sold to scrap merchants but have not yet been broken up, as they could be sold on for reuse.

Finally, those locos moved abroad by the likes of DB Cargo or Freightliner, or sold for use by European operators, are also included here.

Section 3 details all locos classed as 'preserved', regardless of whether they have been restored or not. This includes locos that may have never run, or realistically are unlikely to ever run again. It does *not* include locos located at heritage sites that are owned by FOCs or spot hire companies; these are listed in section 2.

Finally, **section 4** lists all ex-BR locos that have been disposed of – and so no longer physically exist. These are listed in class order with their final number, and all previous numbers are also listed. However, their names are not included, nor are their detail difference and their disposal details.

Three-character owner and livery codes, sector codes and depot allocations are all listed in the appendices. Standard TOPS pool codes are used, but two-digit codes for depots and other locations are also listed.

Locos can, and of course will, change owner or status and so their inclusion in a certain section may change as events overtake them.

There were three or four errors in the first edition that have been corrected, but as always the information in this book is in good faith and, as far as is known, correct to 8 September 2018. Any corrections, input or comments should be sent to the author via the publisher.

Pip Dunn, Spalding, October 2018

Codes for key loco detail differences

Codes for key loco detail differences
  The key differences that affect the work or area that a loco can undertake are detailed. These are given by codes:

a   Train air brakes only
b   Operational steam heat boiler fitted
c   Tripcocks fitted
d   Dellner coupler fitted
e   Operational Electric Train Supply
f   Fire suppressant equipment fitted
g   ERTMS equipment fitted
h   Lickey banker auto coupler fitted
i   Non-operational steam heat boiler retained
j   Buffers fitted – where non standard
l   Scharfenberg coupler fitted
k   Engine stop-start equipment fitted
m   Multiple Working equipment fitted – where non standard
n   Multiple Working equipment removed – where non standard
o   No train heating capability
p   Snowplough brackets fitted (* main line loco fitted with snowploughs)
q   Remote monitoring equipment fitted
r   In-cab Radio Electronic Token Block (RETB) signalling fitted
s   Slow speed control fitted
t   Additional fuel tanks fitted
u   Push-pull fitted
v   Vacuum train brakes only
w   Waist level duplicate brake pipes fitted
x   Dual train brakes
y   Non-operational Electric Train Supply
z   Through Electric Train Supply wiring (loco is 'no heat')

All locos in sections 1 and 2 are deemed to be operational unless stated. All fittings relate to the loco at the time of press.

(S) Loco is in store in a serviceable condition. The loco may not have run for some time but could be returned to traffic relatively quickly. It may be stored pending an upgrade to meet group standards or may have been stopped to temporarily donate parts to another vehicle.

(U) Loco is in store in an unserviceable condition; the loco has been damaged, stripped, or laid up for a long period and would require major expenditure to return it to traffic. It may currently not meet group standards. Some of these locos may be for sale.

For preserved locos they are either classed as either operational (OP), actively under restoration (UR) or stored for parts donation, disposal or restoration to start at a later date (SU). Locos on static display are also listed as SU. D5910 is classed as UC – under construction.

Key abbreviations

AC	Alternating current
DC	Direct current
ETH	Electric Train Heat
ETS	Electric Train Supply
ft	foot
gal	gallon
GSM-R	Global System for Mobile Communications – Railway
hp	Horsepower
in	inch
kN	Kilonewton
kV	kilovolt
kW	kilowatt
km/h	kilometres per hour
lbf	pounds force
lit	litre
m	metre
mph	miles per hour
OTMR	On Train Monitoring and Recording ('black box')
TPWS	Train Protection and Warning System
V	Volt

On hire to GB Railfreight, 20189/205 lead 1Z24, the 1700 Dungeness-Victoria return leg of Pathfinder Tours' 'Diamond Twenties' charter past Snargate, near Appledore on the Dungeness branch, on 5 May 2018. *Anthony Hicks*

1 The main line fleet

Locos are listed by the current TOPS numbers, their previous numbers – including pre-TOPS D numbers, fittings, the sector the loco is allocated to, the owner, livery, depot allocation or location the loco is at, and its current name.

Locos that had 89xxx numbers do NOT have these listed as they are not usually displayed other than in the cabs.

Class 08

Part of the mass order for the Standard BR 0-6-0 diesel electric shunter, of which over 1,000 were built from 1952. Just a handful survive with a few train operators. More locos are owned by spot hire companies and listed in section 2.

Built by:	BR Derby, Crewe, Darlington, Horwich
Years introduced:	1952-62
Wheel arrangement:	0-6-0
Weight:	49-50 tons
Length:	29ft 3in (8.91m)
Engine Type:	English Electric 6KT
Engine output:	400hp (298kW)
Power at rail:	260hp (194kW)
Tractive effort:	35,000lbf (156kN)
Continuous tractive effort	11,100lbf (49kN)
Maximum design speed:	15-20mph (25-33km/h)
Brake Force:	19 tonnes
Route Availability:	5
Main generator type:	EE801-8E or E801-14E
Auxiliary generator type:	EE736-2D, EE736-4E or EE906-3D
Traction Motor type:	EE506-6A or EE506-7C
Fuel tank capacity:	668gal (3,036lit)
Multiple working type:	not fitted

Loco's current TOPS number	Previous official numbers carried	Key detail differences	Current TOPS Sector	Vehicle Owner	Current Livery	Current depot allocation or location	Current name (as displayed on the loco) Minor wording on crests, plaques or graphics is excluded
08410	D3525	ao	EFSH	GWR	GWR	PZ	
08411	D3526	ao	MBDL	RSS	BRW	WI (U)	
08417	D3532	ao	QADD	NET	NRY	DF (U)	
08418	D3533	ao	AWCA	WCR	EWS	CS	
08451	D3566	ao	ATZZ	ALS	BRW	LO	*MA SMITH*
08454	D3569	aod	ATLO	ALS	BRW	WD	
08472	D3587	ao	RFSH	WAB	BLK	EC	
08480	D3595	ao	MBDL	RSS	RSS	NC	
08483	D3598	ao	EFSH	GWR	BLK	LA	
08485	D3600	ao	AWCA	WCR	BRW	CS	
08507	D3662	ao	RTSO	RIV	OXB	BU	
08511	D3673	ao	MBDL	RSS	RSS	CM	
08523	D3685	ao	MRSO	RMS	RMS	IS	
08525	D3687	ao	EMSL	EMT	EMB	NL	*DUNCAN BEDFORD*
08530	D3692	ao	DDIN	POR	FLR	SM	
08531	D3693	ao	DDIN	POR	FPH	LH (S)	
08571	D3738	ao	HBSH	WAB	BLK	FX	
08575	D3742	xo	DHLT	POR	FLR	LH (U)	

08585	D3752	ao	DDIN	POR	FLR	SM	Vicky
08588	D3755	ao	MRSO	RMS	RMS	DF	
08596	D3763	ao	HBSH	WAB	BLK	EC	
08611	D3778	ao	ATLO	ALS	BRW	WB	
08616	D3783	xo	EJLO	LON	LON	TS	TYSELEY 100
08617	D3784	aod	ATLO	ALS	BLK	OX	Steve Purser
08624	D3791	xo	DDIN	POR	FPH	FX	Rambo Paul Ramsey
08631	D3798	xo	MBDL	LSL	BRW	CD	
08641	D3808	ao	EFSH	GWR	BRW	LA	Pride of Laira
08644	D3811	ao	EFSH	GWR	BRW	LA	Laira Diesel Depot 50 Years 1962-2012
08645	D3812	ao	EFSH	GWR	DEP	LA	Mike Baggott
08663	D3830	ao	EFSH	GWR	BRW	PM	St Silas
08670	D3837	ao	MBDL	RSS	RSS	BN	
08678	D3845	ao	AWCX	WCR	WCR	CS	
08683	D3850	ao	MBDL	RSS	EWS	NC	
08690	D3857	ao	EMSL	EMT	EMB	NL	DAVID THIRKILL
08691	D3858	xo	DDIN	FLI	FLG	FX	Terri
08696	D3863	ao	ATLO	ALS	BRW	WB	
08704	D3871	ao	RTSO	LSL	OXB	BU	
08721	D3889	ao	ATLO	ALS	BRW	WD	Longsight TMD
08735	D3903	ao	WQDA	DBC	EWS	EH (U)	
08737	D3905	ao		LSL	EWS	CD	
08780	D3948	xo	MBDL	LSL	BLE	WO	
08785	D3953	ao	DDIN	POR	FLR	TP	
08790	D3958	ao	ATLO	ALS	BRW	EG	
08795	D3963	ao	EFSH	GWR	BLK	LE	Landore
08805	D3973	xo	EJLO	LON	RSR	SI	
08822	D3990	ao	EFSH	GWR	ICS	PM	Dave Mills
08836	D4004	ao	EFSH	GWR	GWR	RG	
08887	D4117	ao	ATZZ	ALS	BRW	PO	
08891	D4121	ao	DHLT	POR	FLR	ZG (U)	
08899	D4129	xo	EMSL	EMT	MID	DY	Midland Counties Railway 175 Years 1839-2014
08908	D4138	ao	EMSL	EMT	EMB	NL	IVAN STEPHENSON
08925	D4155	ao	GBWM	GBR	GWS	WG	
08934	D4164	ao	GBWM	GBR	GWS	DG	
08948	D4178	aol	GPSS	EUK	EUK	TI	
08950	D4180	ao	EMSL	EMT	EMB	LH (U)	DAVID LIGHTFOOT

Note: 08451/795 have buckeye couplers

Note: 08735 has a swinghead coupler and remote control equipment

Note: Not all Class 08/09s are passed to run on the main line and may be restricted to designated areas. TOCs that hire shunting locomotives may have these vehicles swapped occasionally with those listed in section 2

Class 09

Another version of the BR standard shunter, the Class 09s had a higher top speed. Twenty-six were originally built, but 12 were later converted by BR from Class 08s.

Built by:	BR Darlington, Horwich
Years introduced:	1959-62
Wheel arrangement:	0-6-0
Weight:	49 tons
Length:	29ft 3in (8.91m)
Engine Type:	English Electric 6KT
Engine output:	400hp (298kW)
Power at rail:	260hp (194kW)

Tractive effort:	25,000lbf (111kN)
Continuous tractive effort	8,800lbf (39kN)
Maximum design speed:	27mph (34km/h)
Brake Force:	19 tonnes
Route Availability:	5
Main generator type:	EE801-8E or E801-14E
Auxiliary generator type:	EE906-3D
Traction Motor type:	EE506-10C
Fuel tank capacity:	668gal (3,036lit)
Multiple Working type:	Not fitted

09002	D3666	ao	GBWM	GBR	GWS	WG
09007	D3671	aow		LOL	GWS	WN
09009	D3720	ao	GBWM	GBR	GWS	DL

Class 20

An initial 20 English Electric Type 1s were part of the 1955 pilot scheme, leading to a further 208 being built between 1957-68. A handful remain in use on the main line.

Built by:	English Electric Vulcan Foundry or Robert Stephenson & Hawthorns
Years introduced:	1957-68
Wheel arrangement:	Bo-Bo
Weight:	73 tons
Length:	46ft 9in (14.26m)
Engine Type:	English Electric 8SVT Mk 2
Engine output:	1,000hp (746kW)
Power at rail:	770hp (574kW)
Tractive effort:	42,000lbf (187kN)
Continuous tractive effort	25,000lbf (111kN)
Maximum design speed:	75mph (120km/h)
Brake Force:	35 tons
Route Availability:	5
Main generator type:	EE819-3C
Auxiliary generator type:	EE911-2B
Traction Motor type:	EE526/5D (20007), 526/8D (others)
Fuel tank capacity:	380gal (1,727lit)
Multiple Working type:	Blue Star

Class 20/0 – standard locos

20007	D8007	ao	MOLO	MOW	GYP	SK	
20096	D8096	aocp	GBEE	HNR	BRB	BH	*Ian Goddard 1938-2016*
20107	D8107	aocp	GBEE	HNR	BRB	BH	
20118	D8118	aop	GBEE	HNR	RSR	BH	*Saltburn-by-the-Sea*
20132	D8132	aop	GBEE	HNR	RSR	BH	*Barrow Hill Depot*
20142	D8142	xocp	MOLO	MOW	MRM	SK	*SIR JOHN BETJEMAN*
20189	D8189	xop	MOLO	MOW	BRB	SK	
20205	D8305	aop	MOLO	MOW	BRB	SK	
20227	D8327	xop	MOLO	CTL	MRM	SK	*SHERLOCK HOLMES*

Class 20/3 – refurbished locos

Details as per Class 20/0
Route Availability: 5 (20301-305), 6 – 20308-314
Traction Motor type: EE526/5D (20301/312), 526/8D (others)
Fuel tank capacity: 640gal (2,909lit, 20301-305), 1,090gal (4,909lit, 20306-315),
Multiple Working type: DRS system

20301	20047, D8047	aotp	XHSS	DRS	DRC	BH (U)	
20302	20084, D8084	aotp	XHNC	DRS	DRC	KM	
20303	20127, D8127	aotp	XHNC	DRS	DRC	KM	*Max Joule 1958-1999*
20304	20120, D8120	aotp	XHSS	DRS	DRC	BH (U)	
20305	20095, D8095	aotp	XHNC	DRS	DRC	KM	
20308	20187, D8187	aotp	XHSS	DRS	DRC	BH (U)	
20309	20075, D8075	aotp	XHSS	DRS	DRC	BH (U)	
20311	20102, D8102	aotcp	GBEE	HNR	HNO	BH	
20312	20042, D8042	aot	XHSS	DRS	DRC	BH (S)	
20314	20117, D8117	aotcp	GBEE	HNR	HNO	BH	

Note: 20302/303/305 are only expected to be in traffic until December for RHTT operation from York for
the 2018 Autumn, and then are expected to return to store pending developments on their future
requirements on these trains.

Class 20/9 – former Hunslet Barclay locos

Details as per Class 20/0
Traction Motor type: 526/8D

| 20901 | 20101, D8101 | aotcp | GBEE | HNR | GBR | BH |
| 20905 | 20225, D8325 | aotcp | GBEE | HNR | GBR | BH |

Owned by HNRC, but on long-term hire to GB Railfreight, 20901/905 bring up the rear of 7X09, the 1142 Old
Dalby-West Ruislip London Underground stock move, at Melton Mowbray on 6 May 2013. *Anthony Hicks*

Class 31

A derivative of an initial 20-strong order for the 1955 pilot scheme, the fleet eventually totalled 263 locos. All were new with Mirrlees engines but these proved unreliable and all were replaced by EE engines in 1964-69. The pilot scheme locos were all withdrawn by 1980, and 70 were later converted to have ETH. None are currently fit for use on the main line.

Built by:	Brush Ltd, Loughborough
Years introduced:	1964-69 (converted from Class 30s)
Wheel arrangement:	A1A-A1A
Weight:	107-111 tons
Length:	56ft 9in (17.29m)
Engine Type:	English Electric 12SVT
Engine output:	1,470hp (1,097kW)
Power at rail:	1,170hp (872kW)
Tractive effort:	35,900lbf (160kN)
Continuous tractive effort	18,700lbf (83kN)
Maximum design speed:	90mph (144km/h)
Brake Force:	49 tons
Route Availability:	5
Main generator type:	Brush TG160-48
Auxiliary generator type:	Brush TG69-42
Traction Motor type:	Brush TM73-68
Fuel tank capacity:	530gal (2,385lit)
Multiple Working type:	Blue Star

Class 31/1 – standard locos

31105	D5523	ao	QADD	NET	NRY	DF (S)
31190	D5613	xop	HTLX	DCR	GYP	WH (U)
31233	D5660	ao	QADD	NET	NRY	DF (S)

Note: 31233 has additional spotlights and recording cameras fitted at No. 2 end
Note: 31105/233 were offered for sale as this book went to print

Class 31/4 – fitted with ETH

Details as per Class 31/1 except:

ETH generator type:	Brush BL100-30
ETH index:	66
Route Availability:	6

31452	D5809, 31279, 31552	xef	HTLX	DCR	DCG	WO (S)
31454	D5654, 31228, 31554	xef	HTLX	HNR	ICM	WO (U)

Class 33

Type 3 design built by BRCW for the Southern Region, fitted with dual brakes and electric train heat from new. Nineteen locos were converted to push-pull operation (Class 33/1s) and the final 12 were built with a narrower body profile for working on the gauge-restricted Hastings line (Class 33/2).

Built by:	Birmingham RC&W
Years introduced:	1960-62
Wheel arrangement:	Bo-Bo
Weight:	77 tons

Length:	50ft 9in (15.47m)
Engine Type:	Sulzer 8LDA28A
Engine output:	1,550hp (1,154kW)
Power at rail:	1,215hp (906kW)
Tractive effort:	45,000lbf (200kN)
Continuous tractive effort	26,000lbf (116kN)
ETH generator type:	Crompton Parkinson CAG392-A1
ETH index:	48
Maximum design speed:	85mph (137km/h)
Brake Force:	35 tons
Route Availability:	6
Main generator type:	Crompton Parkinson CAG391-B1
Auxiliary generator type:	Crompton Parkinson CAG193-A1
Traction Motor type:	Crompton Parkinson C171-C2
Fuel tank capacity:	750gal (3,410lit)
Multiple Working type:	Blue Star

Class 33/0 – standard locos

33012	D6515	xep	MBDL	SOA	GYP	SR	*Lt Jenny Lewis RN*
33025	D6543	xyp*	AWCA	WCR	WCR	CS	
33029	D6547	aop	AWCA	WCR	WCR	CS	
33030	D6548	ayp	AWCX	WCR	DRU	CS (U)	

Class 33/2 – narrow 'Hastings gauge' body

33207	D6592	aop	AWCA	WCR	WCR	CS	*Jim Martin*

During a two-week spell of locomotive haulage on the Windermere branch, West Coast Railways' 33029 top-and-tails with 57316 on 2Z06, the 1330 Windermere-Oxenholme, passing Plantation Bridge near Staveley on 22 June 22. *Anthony Hicks*

Class 37

Standard Diesel Electric Type 3 design, of which 309 were built. A total of 135 locos were refurbished in the late 1980s, including 31 with ETH (Class 37/4), 44 with added ballast weights (Class 37/7) and six with test bed alternative engines (Class 37/9). Twelve locos were later converted with through ETH wiring for Eurostar.

Built by:	English Electric, Vulcan Foundry or Robert Stephenson & Hawthorns
Years introduced:	1960-65
Wheel arrangement:	Co-Co
Weight:	102-108 tons
Length:	61ft 6in (18.74m)
Engine Type:	English Electric 12CSVT
Engine output:	1,750hp (1,304kW)
Power at rail:	1,250hp (932kW)
Tractive effort:	55,500lbf (247kN)
Continuous tractive effort	35,000lbf (156kN)
Maximum design speed:	90mph (144km/h)
Brake Force:	50 tons
Route Availability:	5
Main generator type:	EE822-10G, EE822-13G or EE822-16J
Auxiliary generator type:	EE911/5C
Traction Motor type:	EE538-1A or EE538-5A
Fuel tank capacity:	890gal (4,046lit) or t – 1,690gal (7,682lit)
Multiple Working type:	Blue Star (DRS system: 37038/059/069/218/259)

Class 37/0 – standard locos

37025	D6725	xbprz*	COTS	STG	BLL	BH	*Inverness TMD*
37038	D6738	aot	XHNC	DRS	DRN	KM	
37057	D6757	xi	COTS	COL	GYP	BH	
37059	D6759	aotr	XHNC	DRS	DRN	KM	
37069	D6769	aotr	XHNC	DRS	DRN	KM	
37099	D6799, 37324	xirp*	COTS	COL	COL	BH	*MERL EVANS 1947-2016*
37116	D6816	xor	COTS	COL	COL	BH	
37146	D6846	xot		COL	CCE	ST (U)	
37165	D6865, 37374	xot		WCR	CCT	CS (U)	
37175	D6875	xorp*	COTS	COL	COL	BH	
37188	D6888	xip		COL	UND	BH (U)	
37207	D6907	aotp		COL	BRB	BH (U)	
37218	D6918	aotrp*	XHNC	DRS	DRN	KM	
37219	D6919	aotrp*	COTS	COL	COL	BH	*Jonty Jarvis 8-12-1998 to 18-3-2005*
37254	D6954	aotrp	COTS	COL	COL	BH	*Cardiff Canton*
37259	D6959, 37380	aotrp	XHNC	DRS	DRC	KM	

Note: 37219 has monitoring equipment mounting brackets fitted at No. 2 end
Note: The planned overhauls on 37146/188/207 have been suspended and the locos may be sold

Class 37/4 – refurbished locos with ETH

Details as per 37/0 except:

Converted by:	BREL Crewe
Years introduced:	1985/86

Preserved by the Scottish Class 37 Group, 37025 *Inverness TMD* has been on long-term hire to Colas Rail Freight for hauling infrastructure monitoring trains. On 3 June 2017 it took a break from this work to partner 37421 on an Edinburgh-Wick charter and is seen at Brora on its return. *Pip Dunn*

Tractive effort:	57,440lbf (256kN)
Continuous tractive effort	41,250lbf (184kN)
ETH alternator type:	Brush BAH701
ETH index:	30
Design speed:	80mph (128km/h)
Main alternator type:	Brush BA1005A
Auxiliary alternator type:	Brush BA606A
Multiple Working type:	Blue Star (DRS system and Blue Star: 37423)

37401	D6968, 37268	aetp*	XHCC	DRS	BLL	KM	*Mary Queen of Scots*
37402	D6974, 37274	aetp*	XHCC	DRS	BLL	KM	*Stephen Middlemore 23.12.1954-8.6.2013*
37403	D6607, 37307	xetfp*	XHCC	SRP	BLL	KM	*Isle of Mull*
37405	D6982, 37282	aerftp*	XHAC	DRS	DRC	KM	
37407	D6605, 37305	aetfp*	XHAC	DRS	BLL	KM	
37409	D6970, 37270	aetfp*	XHAC	DRS	BLL	KM	*Lord Hinton*
37418	D6971, 37271	xetp*	MBDL	BEN	BLL	BH (U)	
37419	D6991, 37291	aerftp*	XHAC	DRS	DRC	KM	*Carl Haviland 1954-2012*
37421	D6967, 37267	aetfp*	COTS	COL	COL	BH	
37422	D6966, 37266	aerftp	XHAC	DRS	DRU	KM	
37423	D6996, 37296	aerftp*	XHAC	DRS	DRX	KM	*Spirit of the Lakes*
37424	D6979, 37279	aetfp*	XHCC	DRS	BLL	KM	*Avro Vulcan XH558*
37425	D6992, 37292	aerftp*	XHCC	DRS	DRC	KM	*Sir Robert McAlpine/ Concrete Bob*

Note: 37424 carries the numbers 37558 on its bodysides
Note: 37418 is to go on hire to Colas Rail Freight

Owned by DRS but painted in retro British Rail 'large logo' colours, 37402 *Stephen Middlemore* hauls Northern Rail's 2C49, 1140 Barrow-Carlisle, past Lady Hall near Foxfield on 2 February 2018. *Anthony Hicks*

Class 37/5 – refurbished locos with no heating

Details as per Class 37/4 except:

Years introduced:	1985-89
Tractive effort:	55,590lbf (248kN)
Multiple Working type:	Blue Star (DRS system and Blue Star: 37667)

37516	D6786, 37086	xotrp*	AWCA	WCR	WCR	CS	*Loch Laidon*
37517	D6718, 37018	xotp	AWCX	WCR	LHO	CS (U)	
37518	D6776, 37076	xotrp*	AWCA	WCR	WCR	CS	
37521	D6817, 37117	xotp*	COTS	SW	COL	BH	

Class 37/6 – refurbished former Eurostar locos

Details as per Class 37/5 except:

Years introduced:	1995-96
Design speed:	90mph (144km/h)
Multiple Working type:	Blue Star (DRS system: 37602/605-611, DRS system and Blue Star: 37601/603/604)

Originally modified with through ETH wiring

37601	D6705, 37005, 37501	aotdrp*	GROG	ROG	EPX	LR		*Perseus*
37602	D6782, 37082, 37502	aotrzp*	XHNC	DRS	DRC	KM		
37603	D6739, 37039, 37504	aotp	XHSS	DRS	DRC	LT (S)		
37604	D6707, 37007, 37506	aotp	XHSS	DRS	DRC	LT (S)		
37605	D6736, 37036, 37507	aotrp	XHNC	DRS	DRC	KM		
37606	D6790, 37090, 37508	aotp*	XHNC	DRS	DRC	KM		
37607	D6803, 37103, 37511	aotpr	COTS	COL	DRU	BH		
37608	D6722, 37022, 37512	aotrp*	GROG	EPX	EPX	LR		*Andromeda*
37609	D6815, 37115, 37514	aotrp*	XHSS	DRS	DRC	LT (S)		
37610	D6871, 37171, 37687	aotrp	COTS	HNR	BLU	BH		
37611	D6881, 37181, 37690	aotdrp*	GROG	EPX	EPX	LR		*Pegasus*
37612	D6879, 37179, 37691	aotpr	COTS	HNR	DRU	BH		

Class 37/5 (continued)

37667	D6851, 37151	aotrp	MBDL	LSL	UND	CD (S)	
37668	D6957, 37257	xotrp	AWCA	WCR	WCR	CS	
37669	D6829, 37129	xotrp	AWCA	WCR	WCR	CS	
37676	D6826, 37126	xotp	AWCA	WCR	WCR	CS (U)	*Loch Rannoch*
37685	D6934, 37234	xotrp*	AWCA	WCR	WCR	CS	*Loch Arkaig*

Class 37/7 – refurbished locos with ballast weights

Details as per Class 37/5 except:

Years introduced:	1986-88
Weight:	120 tons
Tractive effort	62,000lbf (276kN)
Brake Force:	60 tons
Route Availability:	7
Multiple Working type:	Blue Star (DRS system and Blue Star: 37716)

37706	D6716, 37016	xotrp*	AWCA	WCR	WCR	CS	
37710	D6744, 37044	xotp		WCR	LHO	CS (U)	
37712	D6802, 37102	xotp	AWCX	WCR	WCR	CS (U)	
37716	D6794, 37094	aotfp*	XHNC	DRS	DRN	KM	
37800	D6843, 37143	aotdp*	GROG	EPX	EPX	LR	*Cassiopeia*
37884	D6883, 37183	aotp	GROG	EPX	EPX	LR	*Cepheus*

Note: 37884 has a tightlock coupler fitted

Class 37/9 – refurbished locos with trial engines

Details as per Class 37/7 except:

Years introduced:	1986
Engine Type:	37901-904 – Mirrlees MB275T
	37905-906 – Ruston RK270T

Engine output:	1,800hp (1,340kW) – 37901-906
Power at rail:	1,300hp (940kW) – 37901-906
Tractive effort	62,680lbf (279kN)
Multiple Working type:	Blue Star

37901	D6850, 37150	xotp	COLS	EPX	EPX	ZG (U)	*Mirrlees Pioneer*
37905	D6836, 37136	xotp	UKRM	UKR	GYP	LR (S)	
37906	D6906, 37206	xotp	UKRM	UKR	RFO	LR (S)	

Class 97 – Network Rail Class 37/0s with ERTMS
Details as per Class 37/0 except:

Years introduced:	2008
Multiple Working type:	Blue Star

97301	D6800, 37100	xotgp	QETS	NET	NRY	ZA	
97302	D6870, 37170	xotgp*	QETS	NET	NRY	ZA	
97303	D6878, 37178	xotgp*	QETS	NET	NRY	ZA	
97304	D6917, 37217	xotgp	QETS	NET	NRY	ZA	*John Tiley*

Class 40
A pilot scheme of ten locos led to another 190 being ordered. All were withdrawn by 1985 bar the pioneer loco D200 (40122), which was retained for special duties until withdrawal in 1988. 40145 returned to the main line in 2002 and 40013 in 2018.

The Class 40 Preservation Society's 40145 waits at Llandudno before returning to Preston at 1600 with a charter train on 10 June 2017. *Pip Dunn*

Built by:	English Electric, Vulcan Foundry
Years introduced:	1958-62
Wheel arrangement:	1Co-Co1
Length:	69ft 6in (21.18m)
Weight:	136 tons
Engine Type:	English Electric 16SVT Mk 2
Engine output:	2,000hp (1,492kW)
Power at rail:	1,550hp (1,156kW)
Tractive effort:	52,000lb
Continuous tractive effort	30,900lbf (137kN)
Maximum design speed:	90mph (144km/h)
Brake Force:	51 tons
Route Availability:	6
Main generator type:	EE822
Auxiliary generator type:	EE911-2B
Traction Motor type:	EE 526-5D
Fuel tank capacity:	710gal (3,195lit)
Multiple Working type:	Blue Star

40013	D213	xo	HNRS	SW	GYP	CD		*ANDANIA*
40145	D345	xo	CFSL	CFP	BRB	BQ		

Note: 40145 returned to the main line in 2002 and 40013 in 2018.

On 27 August 2018, D213 *Andania* made its return main line charter train work hauling 1Z40, the 0915 Crewe-Carlisle special. It passes Garsdale on the Settle and Carlisle line. *Anthony Hicks*

Class 43

The HST power cars (not to be confused with the Class 43 North British Warship Diesel hydraulics), run in pairs, either end of a rake of Mk 3 trailer vehicles. All were built with Paxman Valenta engines but all were re-engined with either MTU or VP185 engines. Just three have been written off after collisions. The Virgin East Coast and some Great Western Railway power cars will be replaced by Class 800/801/802 multiple units in the next three years. Fifty-four power cars are destined for ScotRail and the transfer of the first locos has started.

Built by:	BREL Crewe
Years introduced:	1976-82
Wheel arrangement:	Bo-Bo
Weight:	70 tons
Length:	58ft 5in (17.80m)
Original engine:	Paxman Valenta 12RP200L (all since removed)
Replacement engines:	Mirrlees Blackstone MB190 (all since removed)
	Paxman 12VP185 (EMPC locos only)
	MTU16V4000 R41R
Engine output:	2,700hp (2,010kW)
Power at rail:	1,770hp (1,320kW)
Tractive effort:	17,980lbf (80kN)
Continuous Tractive effort:	10,340lbf (46kN)
Maximum design speed:	125mph (200km/h)
Brake force	35t
Route Availability:	6
Main alternator type:	Brush BA1001B (VP185 locos), Brush BA1001C (MTU locos)
Traction Motor type:	43002-123/153-198 (Brush TMH68-46), 43124-152 (GECG417AZ)
Fuel tank capacity:	1,030gal (4,680lit)
Multiple Working type:	Within class only

43002	ae	EFPC	ANG	HST	LA	Sir Kenneth Grange
43003	ae	HAPC	ANG	FGU	EC	
43004	ae	EFPC	ANG	GWT	LA	
43005	ae	EFPC	ANG	GWT	LA	
43009	ae	EFPC	ANG	FGB	LA	
43010	ae	EFPC	ANG	FGB	LA	
43012	ae	HAPC	ANG	SCT	EC	
43013	aej	QCAR	POR	NRY	EC	Mark Carne CBE
43014	aej	QCAR	POR	NRY	EC	The Railway Observer
43015	ae	EFPC	ANG	FGB	LA	
43016	ae	EFPC	ANG	GWT	LA	
43017	ae	EFPC	ANG	FGB	LA	Hannahs discoverhannahs.org
43018	ae	EFPC	ANG	FGB	LA	
43020	ae	EFPC	ANG	FGB	LA	mtu Power Passion Partnership
43021	ae	HAPC	ANG	FGU	EC	
43022	ae	EFPC	ANG	FGB	LA	The Duke of Edinburgh's Award Diamond Anniversary 1956-2016
43023	ae	EFPC	ANG	FGB	LA	SQN LDR HAROLD STARR ONE OF THE FEW

43024	ae	EFPC	ANG	FGB	LA	*Great Western Society 1961-2011 Didcot Railway Centre*
43025	ae	EFPC	ANG	FGB	LA	*INSTITUTION OF RAILWAY OPERATORS 2000-2010 TEN YEARS PROMOTING OPERATIONAL EXCELLENCE*
43026	ae	HAPC	ANG	FGU	EC	
43027	ae	EFPC	ANG	FGS	LA	
43028	ae	HAPC	ANG	FGU	EC	
43029	ae	EFPC	ANG	FGB	LA	
43030	ae	EFPC	ANG	FGB	LA	*Christian Lewis Trust*
43031	ae	HAPC	ANG	FGU	EC	
43032	ae	HAPC	ANG	SCT	EC	
43033	ae	HAPC	ANG	SCT	EC	
43034	ae	EFPC	ANG	FGB	LA	*TravelWatch South West*
43035	ae	EFPC	ANG	FGB	LA	
43036	ae	HAPC	ANG	FGU	EC	
43037	ae	HAPC	ANG	FGU	EC	
43040	ae	EFPC	ANG	FGB	LA	*Bristol St Philip's Marsh*
43041	ae	EFPC	ANG	GWT	LE	*Meningitis Trust Support for Life*
43042	ae	EFPC	ANG	GWT	LE	
43043	ae	EMPC	POR	EMB	NL	
43044	ae	EMPC	POR	EMB	NL	
43045	ae	EMPC	POR	EMB	NL	
43046	ae	EMPC	POR	EMB	NL	
43047	ae	EMPC	POR	EMB	NL	
43048	ae	EMPC	POR	EMB	NL	*TCB Miller MBE*
43049	ae	EMPC	POR	EMB	NL	*Neville Hill*
43050	ae	EMPC	POR	EMB	NL	
43052	ae	EMPC	POR	EMB	NL	
43053	ae	EFPC	POR	FGB	LE	*University of Worcester*
43054	ae	EMPC	POR	EMB	NL	
43055	ae	EMPC	POR	EMB	NL	*The Sheffield Star 125 Years*
43056	ae	EFPC	POR	FGB	LE	*The Royal British Legion*
43058	ae	IECP	POR	EMB	NL	
43059	ae	EMPC	POR	EMB	NL	
43060	ae	EMPC	POR	EMB	NL	
43061	ae	IECP	POR	EMB	NL	*The Fearless Foxes*
43062	ae	QCAR	POR	NRY	EC	*John Armitt*
43063	ae	EFPC	POR	FGB	LE	
43064	ae	EMPC	POR	EMB	NL	
43066	ae	EMPC	POR	EMB	NL	
43069	ae	EFPC	POR	FGB	LE	
43070	ae	EFPC	POR	FGB	LE	*The Corps of Royal Electrical & Mechanical Engineers*
43071	ae	EFPC	POR	FGB	LE	
43073	ae	EMPC	POR	EMB	NL	
43075	ae	EMPC	POR	EMB	NL	
43076	ae	EMPC	POR	EMB	NL	*IN SUPPORT OF HELP FOR HEROES*
43078	ae	EFPC	POR	FGB	LE	
43079	ae	EFPC	POR	FGB	LE	
43081	ae	EMPC	POR	EMB	NL	
43082	ae	EMPC	POR	EMB	NL	*RAILWAY Children*

43083	ae	EMPC	POR	EMB	NL	
43086	ae	EFPC	POR	FGB	LE	
43087	ae	EFPC	POR	FGB	LE	*11 Explosive Ordnance Disposal Regiment Royal Logistics Corps*
43088	ae	EFPC	POR	FGB	LE	
43089	ae	EMPC	POR	EMB	NL	
43091	ae	EFPC	POR	FGB	LE	
43092	ae	EFPC	FIR	GWT	LE	
43093	ae	EFPC	FIR	GWA	LE	*Old Oak Common HST Depot 1976-2018*
43094	ae	EFPC	FIR	FGB	LE	
43097	ae	EFPC	FIR	FGB	LE	*Environment Agency*
43098	ae	EFPC	FIR	GWT	LE	
43122	ae	EFPC	FIR	FGB	LE	
43124	ae	EFPC	ANG	FGB	LE	
43125	ae	HAPC	ANG	FGU	EC	
43126	ae	HAPC	ANG	FGU	EC	
43127	ae	HAPC	ANG	FGU	EC	
43128	ae	HAPC	ANG	FGB	EC	
43129	ae	HAPC	ANG	FGU	EC	
43130	ae	EFPC	ANG	FGB	HA	
43131	ae	EFPC	ANG	FGB	LE	
43132	ae	HAPC	ANG	FGU	EC	
43133	ae	EFPC	ANG	FGB	LE	
43134	ae	HAPC	ANG	SCT	EC	
43135	ae	HAPC	ANG	FGU	EC	
43136	ae	EFPC	ANG	FGB	LE	
43137	ae	EFPC	ANG	FGB	LE	*Newton Abbot 150*
43138	ae	EFPC	ANG	FGB	LE	
43139	ae	EFPC	ANG	FGB	HA	
43140	ae	HAPC	ANG	SCT	EC	
43141	ae	HAPC	ANG	FGU	EC	
43142	ae	HAPC	ANG	FGU	EC	
43143	ae	HAPC	ANG	SCT	EC	
43144	ae	EFPC	ANG	FGA	LE	
43145	ae	HAPC	ANG	FGU	EC	
43146	ae	HAPC	ANG	SCT	EC	
43147	ae	EFPC	ANG	FGB	LE	*Royal Marines Celebrating 350 Years*
43148	ae	HAPC	ANG	SCT	EC	
43149	ae	HAPC	ANG	SCT	EC	
43150	ae	EFPC	ANG	FGB	LE	
43151	ae	EFPC	ANG	FGB	LE	
43152	ae	HAPC	ANG	FGU	EC	
43153	ae	EFPC	FIR	FGB	LA	
43154	ae	EFPC	FIR	FGB	LA	
43155	ae	EFPC	FIR	FGB	LA	*The Red Arrows 50 Seasons of Excellence*
43156	ae	EFPC	POR	FGB	LA	*Dartington International Summer School*
43158	ae	EFPC	FIR	FGB	LA	
43159	ae	EFPC	POR	FGB	LA	
43160	ae	EFPC	POR	FGB	LA	*Sir Moir Lockhead OBE*
43161	ae	EFPC	POR	FGB	LA	
43162	ae	EFPC	POR	FGB	LA	
43163	ae	HAPC	ANG	SCT	EC	

43164		ae	EFPC	ANG	FGB	LA	
43165		ae	EFPC	ANG	FGB	LA	*Prince Michael of Kent*
43168		ae	HAPC	ANG	SCT	EC	
43169		ae	HAPC	ANG	SCT	EC	
43170		ae	EFPC	ANG	GWT	LA	
43171		ae	EFPC	ANG	FGB	LA	
43172		ae	EFPC	ANG	HAR	LA	*Harry Patch The last survivor of the trenches*
43174		ae	EFPC	ANG	FGB	LA	
43175		ae	EFPC	ANG	FGB	LA	*GWR 175TH ANNIVERSARY*
43176		ae	EFPC	ANG	FGB	LA	
43177		ae	EFPC	ANG	FGB	LA	
43179		ae	HAPC	ANG	FGU	EC	
43180		ae	EFPC	POR	FGB	LA	
43181		ae	EFPC	ANG	FGB	LA	
43182		ae	EFPC	ANG	FGB	LA	
43183		ae	HAPC	ANG	SCT	EC	
43185		ae	EFPC	ANG	ICS	LA	*Great Western*
43186		ae	EFPC	ANG	FGS	LA	
43187		ae	EFPC	ANG	GWT	LA	
43188		ae	EFPC	ANG	GWT	LA	
43189		ae	EFPC	ANG	GWT	LA	
43190		ae	EFPC	ANG	FGB	LA	
43191		ae	EFPC	ANG	FGB	LA	
43192		ae	EFPC	ANG	FGB	LA	
43193		ae	EFPC	POR	FGB	LA	
43194		ae	EFPC	FIR	GWT	LA	
43195		ae	EFPC	POR	FGB	LA	
43196		ae	EFPC	POR	FGB	LA	
43197		ae	EFPC	POR	FGB	LA	
43198		ae	EFPC	FIR	GWT	LA	

Note: Fifty-four EFPC locomotives are in the process of transferring to First ScotRail in the HAPC pool. They are expected to be 43003/012/015/021/026/028/030-037, 43124-152/163/164/168/169/175-177/179/181-183

Class 43/2
Details as per 43/0 fitted with MTU engines

43206	43006	ae	IECP	ANG	VEC	EC	
43207	43007	ae	EHPC	ANG	XCT	EC	
43208	43008	ae	IECP	ANG	VEC	EC	*Lincolnshire Echo*
43238	43038	ae	IECP	ANG	NRA	EC	*National Railway Museum 40 Years 1975-2015*
43239	43039	ae	IECP	ANG	VEC	EC	
43251	43051	ae	IECP	POR	VEC	EC	
43257	43057	ae	IECP	POR	VEC	EC	*Bounds Green*
43272	43072	ae	IECP	POR	VEC	EC	
43274	43074	ae	IECP	POR	VEC	EC	*Spirit of Sunderland*
43277	43077	ae	IECP	POR	VEC	EC	
43285	43085	ae	EHPC	POR	XCT	EC	
43290	43090	ae	IECP	POR	VEC	EC	*mtu Fascination of Power*
43295	43095	ae	IECP	ANG	VEC	EC	
43296	43096	ae	IECP	ANG	VEC	EC	
43299	43099	ae	IECP	POR	VEC	EC	
43300	43100	ae	IECP	POR	VEC	EC	*Craigentinny*
43301	43101	ae	EHPC	POR	XCT	EC	
43302	43102	ae	IECP	POR	VEC	EC	

43303	43103	ae	EHPC	POR	XCT	EC		
43304	43104	ae	EHPC	ANG	XCT	EC		
43305	43105	ae	IECP	ANG	VEC	EC		
43306	43106	ae	IECP	ANG	VEC	EC		
43307	43107	ae	IECP	ANG	VEC	EC		
43308	43108	ae	IECP	ANG	VEC	EC		*HIGHLAND CHIEFTAIN*
43309	43109	ae	IECP	ANG	VEC	EC		
43310	43110	ae	IECP	ANG	VEC	EC		
43311	43111	ae	IECP	ANG	VEC	EC		
43312	43112	ae	IECP	ANG	VEC	EC		
43313	43113	ae	IECP	ANG	VEC	EC		
43314	43114	ae	IECP	ANG	VEC	EC		
43315	43115	ae	IECP	ANG	VEC	EC		
43316	43116	ae	IECP	ANG	VEC	EC		
43317	43117	ae	IECP	ANG	VEC	EC		
43318	43118	ae	IECP	ANG	VEC	EC		
43319	43119	ae	IECP	ANG	VEC	EC		
43320	43120	ae	IECP	ANG	VEC	EC		
43321	43121	ae	EHPC	POR	XCT	EC		
43357	43157	ae	EHPC	POR	XCT	EC		
43366	43166	ae	EHPC	ANG	XCT	EC		
43367	43167	ae	IECP	ANG	VEC	EC		*DELTIC 50 1955-2005*
43378	43178	ae	EHPC	ANG	XCT	EC		
43384	43184	ae	EHPC	ANG	XCT	EC		
43423	43123	aej	EMPC	ANG	EMR	NL		*VALENTA 1972-2010*
43465	43065	aej	EMPC	ANG	EMR	NL		
43467	43067	aej	EMPC	ANG	EMR	NL		*British Transport Police Nottingham/ Nottinghamshire Fire and Rescue Service*
43468	43068	aej	EMPC	ANG	EMR	NL		
43480	43080	aej	EMPC	ANG	EMR	NL		
43484	43084	aej	EMPC	ANG	EMR	NL		

43274 has 'Spirit of Sunderland' branding
43295 has 'Perth is the Place' branding
43300 has 'Craigentinny 100 1914-2014' branding

London North Eastern Railway now runs all ECML Anglo-Scottish trains after the collapse of the Stagecoach/Virgin operation. 43367 *Deltic 50* pauses at Edinburgh on 24 July 2018 leading the 1200 King's Cross-Inverness 'Highland Chieftain'. 43239 is on the rear. *Pip Dunn*

Class 45

The development of the pilot scheme Class 44s, the last Class 45 was withdrawn in 1989. Since then, 45112 had a spell on the main line but is now stored. However, Locomotive Services has acquired 45118 and it is expected to return to the main line in the fullness of time.

Built by:	BR Crewe
Years introduced:	62
Wheel arrangement:	1Co-Co1
Weight:	135 tons
Length:	67ft 11in (20.7m)
Engine Type:	Sulzer 12LDA28B
Engine output:	2,500hp (1,865kW)
Power at rail:	2,000hp (1,592kW)
Tractive effort:	55,000lb (245kN)
Continuous tractive effort	30,000lbf (133kN)
Maximum design speed:	90mph (144km/h)
Brake Force:	63 tons
Route Availability:	7
Main generator type:	Crompton CG426A1
Auxiliary generator type:	Crompton CAG252A1
Traction Motor type:	Crompton C172A1
Fuel tank capacity:	840gal (3,780lit)
Multiple Working type	not fitted

45118	D67		xe		MBDL	LSL	BRB	BH (U)	*ROYAL ARTILLERYMAN*

Class 47

BR's standard Type 4 diesel electric, 512 were built between 1962-68. Mass withdrawals started in 1986, but a few have found use with some private operators. Thirty-three were rebuilt as Class 57s.

Built by:	Brush, Loughborough and BR Crewe
Years introduced:	1962-68
Wheel arrangement:	Co-Co
Weight:	111-121 tons
Length:	63ft 6in (19.38m)
Engine Type:	Sulzer 12LDA28C
Engine output:	2,580hp (1,922kW)
Power at rail:	2,080hp (1,550kW)
Tractive effort:	60,000lbf (267kN)
Continuous tractive effort	30,000lbf (133kN)
Maximum design speed:	95mph (152km/h)
Brake Force:	60 tons
Route Availability:	6
Main generator type:	Brush TG160-60 Mk 2, TG160-60 Mk 4 or TM172-50 Mk 1
Auxiliary generator type:	Brush TG69-20 or TG69-28 Mk 2
Traction Motor type:	Brush TM64-68 or TM64-68 Mk 1
Fuel tank capacity:	727 (3,273lit), t – 1,308gal (5,887lit)
Multiple Working type (where fitted): Green Circle	

Class 47/0s – standard locos

47194	D1844	aotm	AWCX	WCR	RFD	CS (U)		
47237	D1914	xotm	AWCA	WCR	WCR	CS		
47245	D1922	xotmp*	AWCA	WCR	WCR	CS		
47270	D1971	ao	AWCA	WCR	BRB	CS (S)		SWIFT

Class 47/3 – originally built with no train heating
Details as per Class 47/0 except:
Multiple Working type (where fitted):   Green Circle

47355	D1836	aotm	AWCX	WCR	FRG	CS (U)
47368	D1887	xo		WCR	TTG	CS (U)

Class 47/4 – originally ETH fitted
Details as per Class 47/0 except:
ETH alternator type: Brush BL100-30
ETH index: 66
Fuel tank capacity: 727 (3,273lit), t – 1,230gal (5,537lit)
Multiple Working type (where fitted): DRS system

47492	D1760	xe	AWCX	WCR	RES	CS (U)	
47500	D1943, 47770	xet	AWCX	WCR	WCR	CS (U)	
47501	D1944	aetm	MBDL	LSL	GYP	CD	CRAFTSMAN
47526	D1109	xe		WCR	LLB	CS (U)	
47580	D1762, 47167, 47732	xet	MBDL	SFG	BRF	CS	County of Essex

Note: 47580 is RA7

Class 47/7 – Converted locos for Rail Express Systems
Details as per Class 47/4
Multiple Working type (where fitted): Green Circle or DRS system (47790)

47727	D1629, 47047, 47569	aetm	GBDF	GBR	CAL	RR	Edinburgh Castle/ Caisteal Dhùn Èideann
47739	D1615, 47035, 47594	aetm	GBDF	GBR	GBR	RR	
47746	D1754, 47160, 47605	xet	AWCA	WCR	WCR	CS	Chris Fudge 29.7.70-22.6.10
47749	D1660, 47076, 47625	aetm	GBDF	GBR	COU	RR	CITY OF TRURO
47760	D1617, 47036, 47562, 47672	xetp*	AWCA	WCR	WCR	CS	
47768	D1725, 47490	aet	AWCX	WCR	UND	CS (U)	
47772	D1657, 47537	xet	AWCA	WCR	WCR	CS	Carnforth TMD
47773	D1755, 47541	xetp	MBDL	VIN	GYP	TM	
47776	D1776, 47181, 47578	xet	AWCX	WCR	RES	CS (U)	
47786	D1730, 47138, 47607, 47821	aet	AWCA	WCR	WCR	CS (U)	Roy Castle OBE
47787	D1757, 47163, 47610, 47823	aet	AWCX	WCR	WCR	CS (U)	
47790	D1973, 47272, 47593, 47673	aetmp	MBDL	LSL	UND	CD (U)	
47798	D1656, 47072, 47609, 47834	xet	MBDL	NRM	RTP	YK (S)	Prince William

Note: 47727/739/749 are in the process of being modified to allow them to haul new Bombardier EMUs and have an extra jumper receptacle on their cab fronts

Class 47/4 continued

Multiple Working type (where fitted): Green Circle (47812/815/843/847/848) or DRS system (47802/805/813/832/841)

47802	D1950, 47552	xetm	AWCA	WCR	WCR	CS	
47804	D1965, 47265, 47591, 47792	xet	AWCA	WCR	WCR	CS	
47805	D1935, 47257, 47650	aetm	MBDL	LSL	GYP	CD	*Roger Hosking MA 1925-2013*
47810	D1924, 47247, 47655	aetm	MBDL	LSL	GYP	CD	*Crewe Diesel Depot*
47811	D1719, 47128, 47656	aet	DHLT	LSL	FPG	CD (U)	
47812	D1916, 47239, 47657	aetm	GROG	ROG	OXB	LR	
47813	D1720, 47129, 47658	aetm	GROG	ROG	ROG	LR (S)	
47815	D1748, 47155, 47660	aetm	SROG	ROG	OXB	LR (U)	
47816	D1650, 47066, 47661	aet	DHLT	LSL	FPG	CD (U)	

West Coast Railways' 47772 *Carnforth TMD* pauses at Peterborough on 12 May 2018 while working the 0614 Skegness-Winchester day excursion, with 47760 tailing. *Pip Dunn*

47818	D1917, 47240, 47663	aetm	MBDL	AFS	DRU	ZG (U)	
47826	D1976, 47274, 47637	aet	AWCA	WCR	WCR	CS	
47830	D1645, 47061, 47649	aet	DFLH	FLI	GYP	CB	*BEECHING'S LEGACY*
47832	D1610, 47031, 47560	aetm	AWCA	WCR	WCR	CS	
47841	D1726, 47134, 47622	aetm	MBDL	LSL	DRU	CD (U)	
47843	D1676, 47090, 47623	aetm	SROG	ROG	OXB	LR (U)	
47847	D1774, 47179, 47577	aetm	SROG	ROG	LLB	LR (U)	
47848	D1652, 47068, 47632	aetm	GROG	ROG	OXB	LR (U)	
47851	D1648, 47064, 47639	aet	AWCA	WCR	WCR	CS (S)	
47853	D1733, 47141, 47614	aetm	MBDL	LSL	BRB	CD	
47854	D1972, 47271, 47604, 47674	aetp*	AWCA	WCR	WCR	CS	*Diamond Jubilee*

Class 50

A fleet of 50 Type 4 diesel electrics built in 1967/68 and withdrawn by 1994. The main line survivors are essentially preserved but do find spot hire use.

Built by:	English Electric Vulcan Foundry
Years introduced:	1967-68
Wheel arrangement:	Co-Co
Weight:	117 tons
Length:	68ft 6in (20.87m)
Engine Type:	English Electric 16CSVT
Engine output:	2,700hp (2,014kW)
Power at rail:	2,070hp (1,540kW)
Tractive effort:	48,500lbf (216kN)
Continuous tractive effort	33,000lbf (147kN)
ETH generator type:	EE915-1B
ETH index:	61
Maximum design speed:	100mph (160km/h)
Brake Force:	59 tons
Route Availability:	6
Main generator type:	EE840-4B
Auxiliary generator type:	EE911-5C
Traction Motor type:	EE538-5A
Fuel tank capacity:	1,055gal (4,797lit)
Multiple Working type:	Orange Square

50007	D407	xep	CFOL	CFA	BRB	KR	*Hercules*
50008	D408	xep	HTLX	GAR	LAB	LR	*Thunderer*
50017	D417	xep	BREL	BOD	NSO	NE	*Royal Oak*
50044	D444	xep	CFOL	CFA	BRB	KR	*Exeter*
50049	D449, 50149	xep*	CFOL	CFA	BRL	KR	*Defiance*
50050	D400	xep	BREL	BOD	BRB	NE	*Fearless*

Privately owned, but usually hired by Rail Operations Group, 50008 *Thunderer* leads 4Z01, the 1210 Thoresby Colliery Junction-Derby RTC rail grinder move, away from Derby station on 4 August 2017. *Anthony Hicks*

Class 52

Type 4 diesel hydraulic design, with 74 locos built but all withdrawn by 1977. The sole main line survivor, one of seven that are preserved, is used mostly on occasional charter trains and is not in day-to-day use.

Built by:	BR Swindon or Crewe
Years introduced:	1961-64
Wheel arrangement:	C-C
Weight:	108 tons
Length:	68ft (20.73m)
Engine Type:	two Maybach MD655
Total Engine output:	2,700hp (2,014kW)
Power at rail:	2,350hp (1,753kW)
Tractive effort:	66,700lbf (297kN)
Continuous tractive effort	45,200lbf (201kN)
Maximum design speed:	90mph (144km/h)
Brake Force:	82 tons
Route Availability:	6
Transmission type:	Voith L630rU
Fuel tank capacity:	850gal (3,825lit)
Multiple Working type:	None

D1015	xo	MBDL	DTG	MFY	KR	*WESTERN CHAMPION*

Class 55

An English Electric twin-engine Type 5 passenger design, just 22 were built for ECML work. All were withdrawn by 1982. Six survivors are preserved but see occasional spot hire use. Just 55009 is currently working on both engines.

Built by:	English Electric, Vulcan Foundry
Years introduced:	1961-62
Wheel arrangement:	Co-Co
Weight:	100 tons
Length:	69ft 6in (21.18m)
Engine Type:	two Napier D18-25 'Deltic'
Engine output:	3,300hp (2,460kW)
Power at rail:	2,460hp (1,969kW)
Tractive effort:	50,000lbf (222kN)
Continuous tractive effort	30,500lbf (136kN)
ETH index:	66
Maximum design speed:	100mph (160km/h)
Brake Force:	51 tons
Route Availability:	5
Main generator type:	two English Electric EE829-1A
Auxiliary generator type:	two English Electric EE913-1A
Traction Motor type:	English Electric EE538A
Fuel tank capacity:	826gal (3,717lit), 1,626gal (7,317lit) – 55022
Multiple Working type:	None

55002	D9002	xe	DBLX	NRM	GYP	YK (S)	THE KING'S OWN YORKSHIRE LIGHT INFANTRY
55009	D9009	xe	DBLX	DPS	BRB	BH	ALYCIDON
55016	D9016	xei	MBDL	LSL	GYE	CD (U)	GORDON HIGHLANDER
55022	D9000	xet	MBDL	LSL	BRB	CD (U)	ROYAL SCOTS GREY

The last Class 55s were withdrawn by British Rail in 1982 but five of the six survivors have spent spells registered for main line use. D9009 *Alycidon* stands at the buffer stops at King's Cross on 16 June 2018 having arrived with the 0435 52A Charters' special from Linlithgow. *Pip Dunn*

Class 56

Type 5 freight loco built from 1976 to 1984. First 30 locos were built in Romania, remainder built at Doncaster and Crewe. Withdrawn by EWS in March 2004, a few have found use with spot hire companies, DC Rail and Colas Rail Freight.

Built by:	Electroputere in Craiovia Romania, BREL Doncaster and Crewe.
Years introduced:	1976-84
Wheel arrangement:	Co-Co
Weight:	126 tons
Length:	63ft 6in (19.39m)
Engine Type:	Ruston Paxman 16RK3CT
Engine output:	3,250hp (2,420kW)
Power at rail:	2,400hp (1,790kW)
Tractive effort:	61,800lbf (275kN)
Continuous tractive effort	53,950lbf (240kN)
Maximum design speed:	80mph (128km/h)
Brake Force:	60 tons
Route Availability:	7
Main alternator type:	Brush BA1101A
Auxiliary alternator type:	Brush BAA602A
Traction Motor type:	Brush TMH73-62
Fuel tank capacity:	1,150gal (5,228lit)
Multiple Working type:	Red Diamond

56007		aos	UKRS	GBR	FER	LR (U)	
56009		aos		GBR	BLE	ZW (U)	
56018		aos	UKRS	GBR	FER	CA (U)	
56031		aos	GBGS	GBR	FER	ZW (U)	
56032		aos	GBGS	GBR	FER	ZW (U)	
56037		aos	GBGS	GBR	EWS	ZW (U)	
56038		aos	UKRS	GBR	FER	LR (U)	
56049		aos	COFS	COL	COL	NE	*Robin of Templecombe 1938-2013*
56051		aos	COLS	COL	COL	NE (U)	
56060		aos	UKRS	GBR	FER	LR (U)	
56065		aos	UKRS	GBR	FER	LR (U)	
56069		aos		GBR	FER	ZW (U)	
56077		aos	UKRS	GBR	LHO	LR (U)	
56078		aos	COFS	COL	COL	NE	
56081		aos	UKRL	GBR	UKG	CA (S)	
56087		aos	COFS	COL	COL	NE (U)	
56090		aos	COFS	COL	COL	NE	
56091		aos	HTLX	UKR	FEU	NE	
56094		aos	COFS	COL	COL	WH	
56096		aos	COFS	COL	COL	WH	
56098		aos	UKRL	GBR	RFO	CA (S)	
56103		aos	HTLX	UKR	DCN	WO	
56104		aos	UKRL	GBR	UKG	CA (S)	
56105		aos	COFS	COL	COL	NE	
56106		aos	UKRS	GBR	UKG	LR (U)	
56113		aos	COFS	COL	COL	NE	
56128		aos		GBR	TRN	ZW (U)	
56301	56045	aos	UKRL	CFS	JFU	CA (S)	

Colas Rail Freight is the main user of Class 56s, with nine in its operational fleet. 56090 and 56094 top-and-tail 6C52, the 0740 Sheffield-Doncaster infrastructure train, past Warmsworth on 15 July 2018. *Anthony Hicks*

56302	56124	aos	COFS	COL	COL	NE	*PECO The Railway Modeller 2016 70 years*
56303	56125	aos	HTLX	UKR	DCG	LR (U)	
56311	56057	aos	GBGS	GBR	DCR	ZW (U)	
56312	56003	aos	HTLX	GBR	DCR	CA (U)	

Locos owned by GB Railfreight are being evaluated for a re-engineering programme that may see some or all fitted with new engines. At the time of going to press, no contracts had been signed or approval for the project signed off.

Class 57

Brush-built locos using the bodies and bogies from redundant Class 47s and re-engineered with second-hand GM engines. Initial order was with Freightliner, for up to 30 locos, but cut back to 12. 57601 was a demonstrator ETH version, later sold to WCR while Virgin Trains ordered 16 and First Great Western four. Six 57/3 were briefly with Network Rail and three 57/0s were briefly with Advenza. The fleet is now split between DRS, GWR and WCR.

Rebuilt by: Brush Traction
Years introduced: 1998-99
Wheel arrangement: Co-Co
Weight: 121 tons
Length: 63ft 6in (19.38m)
Engine Type: General Motors 645-12E3
Engine output: 2,500hp (1,860kW)
Power at rail: 2,025hp (1,507kW)

Tractive effort:	55,000lbf (245kN)
Continuous tractive effort	31,500lbf (140kN)
Maximum design speed:	75mph (121km/h)
Brake Force:	80 tons
Route Availability:	6
Main alternator type:	Brush BA1101A
Auxiliary alternator type:	Brush BAA602A
Traction Motor type:	Brush TM68-46
Fuel tank capacity:	1,221gal (5,550lit)
Multiple Working type:	Green Circle (where fitted)

Class 57/0 – original locos built for Freightliner without train heating

57001	D1875, 47356	ao	AWCA	WCR	WCR	BU (U)	
57002	D1803, 47322	aom	XHCK	DRS	DRN	KM	*RAIL Express*
57003	D1798, 47317	aom	XHCK	DRS	DRN	KM	
57004	D1828, 47347	aom	XHSS	DRS	DRC	LT (S)	
57005	D1831, 47350	ao	AWCX	WCR	ADZ	CS (U)	
57006	D1837, 47187	ao	AWCX	WCR	WCR	CS (U)	
57007	D1813, 47332	aom	XHCK	DRS	DRN	KM	*John Scott 12.5.45-22.5.12*
57008	D1644, 47060	aom	XHSS	DRS	DRC	LT (S)	
57009	D1664, 47079	aom	XHSS	DRS	DRC	LT (S)	
57010	D1907, 47231	aom	XHSS	DRS	DRN	LT (S)	
57011	D1810, 47329	aom	XHSS	DRS	DRC	LT (U)	
57012	D1854, 47204	aom	XHSS	DRS	DRC	LT (S)	

Class 57/3 – ETH locos originally ordered by Virgin Trains

Years introduced	2002-04
Engine Type:	General Motors 645-12F3B
Engine output:	2,750hp (2,051kW)
Power at rail:	2,200hp (1,640kW)
Weight:	117 tons
Main alternator type:	Brush BA1101F or BA1101G
ETH alternator type:	Brush BAA
ETH index:	100
Maximum design speed:	95mph (153km/h)
Brake Force:	60 tons
Fuel tank capacity:	1,308gal (5,887lit)
Multiple Working type:	None

57301	D1653, 47069, 47638, 47845	aedr	XHAC	POR	DRN	KM	*Goliath*
57302	D1928, 47251, 47589, 47827	aed	XHSS	DRS	DRC	ZG (S)	*Chad Varah*
57303	D1957, 47554, 47705	aed	XHAC	POR	DRN	KM	*Pride of Carlisle*
57304	D1639, 47055, 47652, 47807	aed	XHVT	DRS	DRN	KM	*Pride of Cheshire*
57305	D1758, 47164, 47571, 47822	aed	XHAC	POR	NOB	KM	*Northern Princess*
57306	D1919, 47242, 47659, 47814	aed	XHAC	POR	DRN	KM	*Her Majesty's Railway Inspectorate 175*
57307	D1901, 47225	aed	XHVT	DRS	DRN	KM	*LADY PENELOPE*

A handful of ex-Virgin Trains Class 57/3s are now used by DRS and still deployed at strategic locations on the West Coast Main Line to rescue any failed trains. 57307 *Lady Penelope* was on standby at Carlisle on 26 July 2018. *Pip Dunn*

57308	D1677, 47091, 47647, 47846	aed	XHVT	DRS	DRN	KM	*James Ferguson*
57309	D1931, 47254, 47651, 47806	aed	XHVT	DRS	DRN	KM	*Pride of Crewe*
57310	D1618, 47037, 47563, 47831	aedr	XHAC	POR	DRN	KM	*Pride of Cumbria*
57311	D1611, 47032, 47662, 47817	aed	XHSS	DRS	DRC	LT (S)	*Thunderbird*
57312	D1811, 47330	aedr	XHAC	POR	NOB	KM	*Solway Princess*
57313	D1890, 47371	ae	AWCA	WCR	WCR	CS	
57314	D1891, 47372	ae	AWCA	WCR	WCR	CS	
57315	D1911, 47234	ae	AWCA	WCR	WCR	CS	
57316	D1992, 47290	ae	AWCA	WCR	WCR	CS	

57307 has '20 years of Direct Rail Services' branding
57305/312 are to go on sub lease to ROG

Class 57/6 – locos fitted with ETH

Details as per Class 57/3 except:

Years introduced	2001
Weight:	113 tons
Main alternator type:	Brush BA1101E
ETH index:	95
Fuel tank capacity:	727gal (3,273lit)

57601	D1759, 47165, 47590, 47825	ae	AWCA	WCR	NOB	CS	*Windsor Castle*

Working the regular summer Saturdays additional train, 57603 *Tintagel Castle* works 2E75, the 1335 Plymouth-Exeter past South Brent on 15 July 2017. This train is not expected to run with a Class 57 in 2019. *Anthony Hicks*

57602	D1818, 47337	aep*	EFOO	POR	GWT	OO	*Restormel Castle*
57603	D1830, 47349	aep*	EFOO	POR	GWT	OO	*Tintagel Castle*
57604	D1859, 47209	aep*	EFOO	POR	GWR	OO	*PENDENNIS CASTLE*
57605	D1856, 47206	aep*	EFOO	POR	GWT	OO	*Totnes Castle*

Class 59

The first four Class 59/0s, owned by Foster Yeoman, were the first privately owned main line diesels to run on BR, in 1986. FY later ordered a fifth loco while ARC ordered four 59/1s, which were delivered in 1990, and National Power ordered six Class 59/2s. The latter are now owned by DB Cargo. 59003 spent 1997-2014 in Germany until bought by GB Railfreight.

Built by:	GM-EMD, La Grange, Illinois, USA
Years introduced:	1985-95
Wheel arrangement:	Co-Co
Weight:	121 tons
Length:	70ft (21.40m)
Engine Type:	EMD 16-645E3C
Engine output:	3,000hp (2,238kW)
Power at rail:	2,533hp (1,889kW)
Tractive effort:	113,550lbf (506kN)
Continuous tractive effort	65,300lbf (291kN)
Maximum design speed:	60mph (96km/h)
Brake Force:	69 tons
Route Availability:	7

Traction alternator:	EMD AR11
Companion alternator:	EMD D14A
Auxiliary alternator:	EMD 3A8147
Traction Motor type:	EMD D77B
Fuel tank capacity:	1,000gal (4,546lit)
Multiple Working type:	AAR

Class 59/0 – original Foster Yeoman locos

59001	aos	XYPO	AGI	AGI	MD	YEOMAN ENDEAVOUR
59002	aos	XYPO	AGI	AGI	MD	ALAN J DAY
59003	aos	GBYH	GBR	GBR	RR	YEOMAN HIGHLANDER
59004	aos	XYPO	AGI	AGI	MD	PAUL A HAMMOND
59005	aos	XYPO	AGI	AGI	MD	KENNETH J PAINTER

In Aggregates Industries livery, 59001 *Yeoman Endeavour* passes Great Bedwyn on 2 July 2018, working 6C76, the 1439 Acton-Whatley Quarry Mendip Rail stone empties. *Martin Loader*

Class 59/1 – original ARC locos

59101	aos	XYPA	HAN	HAN	MD	Village of Whatley
59102	aos	XYPA	HAN	HAN	MD	Village of Chantry
59103	aos	XYPA	HAN	HAN	MD	Village of Mells
59104	aos	XYPA	HAN	HAN	MD	Village of Great Elm

DB Cargo's 59204 passes through Sonning Cutting while hauling 7A09, the 0712 Merehead-Acton, on 12 August 2016. This scene has now changed dramatically following electrification of the GWML. *Anthony Hicks*

Class 59/2 – original National Power locos

59201	aos	WDAM	DBC	DBC	MD	
59202	aos	WDAM	DBC	DBC	MD	*Alan Meddows Taylor MD Mendip Rail Limited*
59203	aos	WDAM	DBC	DBC	MD	
59204	aos	WDAM	DBC	DBC	MD	
59205	aos	WDAM	DBC	DBC	MD	
59206	aos	WDAM	DBC	DBC	MD	*John F Yeoman Rail Pioneer*

Class 60

Heavy freight Type 5 built by Brush, the last diesel locos delivered to BR. All inherited by EWS (Now DB Cargo). The fleet has been steadily run down since 2004 with ten locos sold to Colas Rail Freight and since sold on to GB Railfreight. DBC retains a fluctuating fleet of about 20 overhauled locos but most of the fleet are now withdrawn.

Built by:	Brush Traction, Loughborough
Years introduced:	1989-93
Wheel arrangement:	Co-Co
Weight:	129-130 tons
Length:	70ft (21.34m)
Engine Type:	Mirrlees MB275T
Engine output:	3,100hp (2,240kW)
Power at rail:	2,415hp (1,800kW)

Tractive effort:	106,500lbf (500kN)
Continuous tractive effort	71,570lbf (336kN)
Maximum design speed:	62mph (99km/h)
Brake Force:	74 tons
Route Availability:	7
Main alternator type:	Brush BA1000
Auxiliary alternator type:	Brush BAA700
Traction Motor type:	Brush TM216
Fuel tank capacity:	990gal (4,500lit)
Multiple Working type:	Within Class only

60001	aos	WCAT	DBC	DBC	TO	
60002	aost	GBTG	BEA	COL	PG	
60003	aost	WQDA	DBC	EWS	TO (U)	*FREIGHT TRANSPORT ASSOCIATION*
60004	aost	WQDA	DBC	EWS	TY (U)	
60005	aost	WQDA	DBC	EWS	TY (U)	
60006	aos	WQDA	DBC	COR	TY (U)	
60007	aost	WCBT	DBC	DBC	TO	*The Spirit of Tom Kendall*
60008	aos	WQDA	DBC	EWS	TC (U)	*Sir William McAlpine*
60009	aost	WQBA	DBC	EWS	TC (U)	
60010	aost	WCBT	DBC	DBC	TO	
60011	aos	WCAT	DBC	DBC	TO (U)	
60012	aost	WQBA	DBC	EWS	TC (U)	
60013	aos	WQDA	DBC	TEW	TO (U)	*Robert Boyle*
60014	aos	WQDA	DBC	TEW	TY (U)	
60015	aost	WCBT	DBC	DBU	TO	
60017	aost	WCBT	DBC	DBC	TO	
60018	aos	WQDA	DBC	EWS	TY (U)	
60019	aos	WCAT	DBC	DBC	TO	*Port of Grimsby & Immingham*
60020	aost	WCBT	DBC	DBC	TO	*The Willows*
60021	aost	GBTG	BEA	COL	PG	
60022	aost	WQDA	DBC	EWS	TO (U)	
60023	aost	WQDA	DBC	EWS	TY (U)	
60024	aos	WQAB	DBC	DBC	TO (U)	*Clitheroe Castle*
60025	aost	WQDA	DBC	EWS	TY (U)	
60026	aost	GBTG	BEA	COL	PG	
60027	aost	WQDA	DBC	EWS	TY (U)	
60028	aost	WQCA	DBC	TEW	CE (U)	
60029	aos	WQCA	DBC	EWS	CE (U)	
60030	aost	WQDA	DBC	EWS	TO (U)	
60031	aos	WQDA	DBC	EWS	TY (U)	
60032	aos	WQDA	DBC	TRN	TY (U)	
60033	aost	WQCA	DBC	COR	TC (U)	*Tees Steel Express*
60034	aos	WQBA	DBC	TEW	TO (U)	*Carnedd Llewelyn*
60035	aos	WQAB	DBC	EWS	TO (U)	
60036	aos	WQBA	DBC	EWS	TO (U)	*GEFCO*
60037	aost	WQDA	DBC	EWS	TY (U)	
60038	aost	WQCA	DBC	EWS	CE (U)	
60039	aos	WCAT	DBC	DBC	TO	*Dove Holes*
60040	aos	WCAT	DBC	DBC	TO	*The Territorial Army Centenary*
60041	aost	WQCA	DBC	EWS	TC (U)	
60042	aos	WQDA	DBC	EWS	TY (U)	

60043	aos	WQBA	DBC	EWS	TO (U)	
60044	aos	WCAT	DBC	DBC	TO	Dowlow
60045	aos	WQBA	DBC	EWS	TC (U)	The Permanent Way Institution
60046	aost	WQCA	DBC	TEW	CE (U)	
60047	aos	GBTG	BEA	COL	PG	
60048	aos	WQCA	DBC	EWS	TO (U)	
60049	aos	WQBA	DBC	EWS	TO (U)	
60050	aos	WQDA	DBC	EWS	TY (U)	
60051	aost	WQDA	DBC	EWS	TO (U)	
60052	aost	WQDA	DBC	EWS	TO (U)	Glofa Tŵr The last deep mine in Wales Tower Colliery
60053	aos	WQBA	DBC	EWS	TY (U)	
60054	aost	WCBT	DBC	DBC	TO	
60055	aost	WQCA	DBC	TEW	CE (U)	
60056	aost	GBTG	BEA	COL	PG	
60057	aos	WQBA	DBC	TEW	TO (U)	Adam Smith
60058	aost	WQBA	DBC	EWS	TO (U)	
60059	aost	WCBT	DBC	DBC	TO	Swinden Dalesman
60060	aos	WQBA	DBC	TEW	TY (U)	
60061	aos	WQCA	DBC	TRN	TC (U)	
60062	aos	WCAT	DBC	DBC	TO	Stainless Pioneer
60063	aos	WCAT	DBC	DBC	TO	
60064	aost	WQBA	DBC	TEW	TO (U)	Back Tor
60065	aos	WCAT	DBC	EWS	TO	SPIRIT OF JAGUAR
60066	aos	WCAT	DBC	DRA	TO	
60067	aos	WQBA	DBC	TEW	TY (U)	
60068	aos	WQBA	DBC	TEW	TO (U)	
60069	aos	WQBA	DBC	EWS	TC (U)	Slioch
60070	aost	WQBA	DBC	TLH	TO (U)	
60071	aost	WQBA	DBC	EWS	TO (U)	Ribblehead Viaduct
60072	aos	WQBA	DBC	TEW	TC (U)	
60073	aos	WQBA	DBC	TEW	TO (U)	Cairn Gorm
60074	aos	WQAA	DBC	DBC	TO (U)	
60075	aos	WQBA	DBC	EWS	TC (U)	
60076	aos	GBTG	BEA	COL	PG	
60077	aost	WQBA	DBC	TEW	TC (U)	
60078	aos	WQBA	DBC	MEW	TY (U)	
60079	aos	WQAB	DBC	DBC	TO (U)	
60080	aost	WQBA	DBC	EWS	TO (U)	
60081	aost	WQBA	DBC	GWR	TY (U)	
60082	aos	WQBA	DBC	TEW	CE (U)	
60083	aos	WQBA	DBC	EWS	TY (U)	
60084	aos	WQBA	DBC	TEW	TC (U)	
60085	aos	GBTG	BEA	COL	PG	
60086	aos	WQBA	DBC	TEW	TY (U)	
60087	aos	GBTG	BEA	COL	PG	
60088	aos	WQBA	DBC	TEW	TY (U)	
60089	aost	WQBA	DBC	EWS	TY (U)	
60090	aost	WQBA	DBC	TEW	TC (U)	
60091	aost	WCBT	DBC	DBC	TO	Barry Needham
60092	aost	WQAA	DBC	DBC	TO (S)	
60093	aos	WQBA	DBC	EWS	TY (U)	
60094	aos	WQBA	DBC	EWS	TC (U)	Rugby Flyer
60095	aos	GBTG	BEA	GBR	PG	
60096	aost	GBTG	BEA	COL	PG	

DB Cargo 60044 *Dowlow* hauls 6M57, the 1104 Lindsey-Kingsbury, past Conisbrough, near Doncaster, on 13 May 2018. *Anthony Hicks*

60097		aost	WQBA	DBC	EWS	TY (U)	
60098		aost	WQBA	DBC	EWS	TO (U)	
60099		aos	WQBA	DBC	TAS	TO (U)	
60100		aos	WCAT	DBC	DBC	TO	Midland Railway - Butterley
60500	60016	aos	WQBA	DBC	EWS	TO (U)	

Note: 60007 has 'SWITCH ON TO SAFETY' branding

Class 66

EWS ordered 250 locos in 1996 that were delivered in 1998-2000, and since then Freightliner, GBRf, DRS and Fastline Freight (now defunct) placed orders. DBC has moved many locos to France and Poland while Freightliner has also redeployed some locos to Poland. Some have been renumbered and three written off.

Built by:	General Motors, London, Canada or EMD Muncie Indiana USA
Years introduced:	1998-2000
Wheel arrangement:	Co-Co
Weight:	126 tons
Length:	70ft 1in (21.40m)
Engine Type:	GM 12N-710G3B-EC
Engine output:	3,300hp (2,462kW)
Power at rail:	3,000hp (2,238kW)
Maximum tractive effort:	92,000lbf (409kN)
Continuous tractive effort:	58,390lbf (260kN)
Maximum design speed:	75mph (120km/h)
Brake Force:	68 tons

Route Availability:	7
Traction alternator:	GM-EMD AR8
Companion alternator:	GM-EMD CA6
Traction Motor type:	GM-EMD D43TR
Fuel tank capacity:	1,440gal (6,550lit)
Multiple Working type:	AAR

Class 66/0 – locos ordered by EWS (Now DB Cargo)

66001	aosck	WBAR	DBC	DBS	TO	
66002	aos	WBAE	DBC	EWS	TO	
66003	aos	WQAA	DBC	EWS	TO (S)	
66004	aosk	WBAE	DBC	EWS	TO	
66005	aos	WBAT	DBC	EWS	TO	
66006	aos	WBAE	DBC	EWS	TO	
66007	aoskq	WBAR	DBC	EWS	TO	
66009	aosk	WBAE	DBC	DBC	TO	
66011	aosk	WBAE	DBC	EWS	TO	
66012	aosk	WBAE	DBC	EWS	TO	
66013	aosk	WBAE	DBC	EWS	TO	
66014	aosk	WBAR	DBC	EWS	TO	
66015	aosk	WBAR	DBC	EWS	TO	
66017	aosckq	WBAR	DBC	DBS	TO	
66018	aosk	WBAE	DBC	DBC	TO	
66019	aosckq	WQAA	DBC	DBS	TO (S)	
66020	aosk	WBAE	DBC	DBC	TO	
66021	aoskq	WBAR	DBC	DBC	TO	
66023	aos	WBAT	DBC	EWS	TO	
66024	aosk	WBAE	DBC	EWS	TO	
66025	aoskq	WBAR	DBC	EWS	TO	
66027	aos	WBAE	DBC	DBC	TO	
66030	aosq	WBAR	DBC	EWS	TO	
66031	aos	WBAT	DBC	EWS	TO	
66034	aosk	WBAE	DBC	DBC	TO	
66035	aosk	WBAE	DBC	DBC	TO	*Resourceful*
66037	aoskq	WBAR	DBC	EWS	TO	
66039	aosk	WBAE	DBC	EWS	TO	
66040	aoskq	WBAR	DBC	EWS	TO	
66041	aosk	WBAE	DBC	DBC	TO	
66043	aosk	WQAA	DBC	EWS	TO (U)	
66044	aosk	WBAE	DBC	DBC	TO	
66047	aos	WBAT	DBC	EWS	TO	
66050	aosk	WBAE	DBC	EWS	TO	*EWS Energy*
66051	aoskq	WQAA	DBC	EWS	TO (S)	
66053	aosk	WBAE	DBC	EWS	TO	
66054	aoskq	WBAR	DBC	EWS	TO	
66055	aoshkq	WBAR	DBC	DBC	TO	*Alain Thauvette*
66056	aoshk	WBLE	DBC	EWS	TO	
66057	aoshk	WBLE	DBC	EWS	TO	
66059	aoshk	WBLE	DBC	EWS	TO	
66060	aos	WBAT	DBC	EWS	TO	
66061	aosk	WBAE	DBC	EWS	TO	
66063	aosk	WBAE	DBC	EWS	TO	
66065	aoskq	WBAR	DBC	DBC	TO	
66066	aoskq	WBAR	DBC	DBC	TO	*Geoff Spencer*
66067	aoskq	WBAR	DBC	EWS	TO	

66068	aosk	WBAR	DBC	EWS	TO	
66069	aosq	WBAR	DBC	EWS	TO	
66070	aos	WBAT	DBC	EWS	TO	
66074	aosk	WBAE	DBC	DBC	TO	
66075	aos	WBAT	DBC	EWS	TO	
66076	aosk	WBAE	DBC	EWS	TO	
66077	aoskq	WBAR	DBC	EWS	TO	*Benjamin Gimbert G.C.*
66078	aosk	WBAE	DBC	EWS	TO	
66079	aosq	WBAR	DBC	EWS	TO	*James Nightall G.C.*
66080	aosk	WBAE	DBC	EWS	TO	
66082	aosk	WBAE	DBC	DBC	TO	
66083	aoskq	WBAR	DBC	EWS	TO	
66084	aosk	WBAR	DBC	EWS	TO	
66085	aoskq	WBAR	DBC	DBC	TO	
66086	aos	WBAE	DBC	EWS	TO	
66087	aosk	WBAE	DBC	EWS	TO	
66088	aosk	WBAE	DBC	EWS	TO	
66089	aoskq	WBAR	DBC	EWS	TO	
66090	aosk	WBAE	DBC	EWS	TO	
66091	aosk	WBAR	DBC	EWS	TO	
66092	aosk	WBAE	DBC	EWS	TO	
66093	aosk	WBAE	DBC	EWS	TO	
66094	aosk	WBAE	DBC	EWS	TO	
66095	aosk	WBAE	DBC	EWS	TO	
66096	aosk	WBAR	DBC	EWS	TO	
66097	aosk	WBAE	DBC	DBS	TO	
66098	aosk	WBAE	DBC	EWS	TO	
66099	aosrk	WBBE	DBC	EWS	TO	
66100	aosrk	WBBE	DBC	EWS	TO	
66101	aosrk	WBBE	DBC	DBS	TO	
66102	aosrk	WBBE	DBC	EWS	TO	
66103	aosrk	WBBE	DBC	EWS	TO	
66104	aosrkq	WBAR	DBC	EWS	TO	
66105	aosrk	WBAR	DBC	EWS	TO	
66106	aosrk	WBBE	DBC	EWS	TO	
66107	aosrkq	WBAR	DBC	EWS	TO	
66108	aosrk	WBBE	DBC	EWS	TO	
66109	aosq	WBAR	DBC	EWS	TO	
66110	aosrk	WBBE	DBC	EWS	TO	
66111	aosr	WBBT	DBC	EWS	TO	
66112	aosrk	WBBE	DBC	EWS	TO	
66113	aosrk	WBBE	DBC	EWS	TO	
66114	aosrk	WBBE	DBC	DBS	TO	
66115	aos	WQAA	DBC	DBC	TO (S)	
66116	aosk	WBAE	DBC	EWS	TO	
66117	aosk	WBAE	DBC	EWS	TO	
66118	aosk	WBAE	DBC	DBS	TO	
66119	aosk	WBAE	DBC	EWS	TO	
66120	aosk	WQAA	DBC	EWS	TO (S)	
66121	aosk	WQAA	DBC	EWS	TO (S)	
66122	aosk	WBAE	DBC	EWS	TO	
66124	aoskq	WBAR	DBC	DBC	TO	
66125	aosk	WBAE	DBC	EWS	TO	
66126	aosk	WBAE	DBC	EWS	TO	
66127	aos	WBAT	DBC	EWS	TO	
66128	aosk	WBAE	DBC	DBC	TO	

66129	aoskq	WBAR	DBC	EWS	TO	
66130	aoskq	WBAR	DBC	DBC	TO	
66131	aos	WBAT	DBC	DBC	TO	
66133	aosk	WQAA	DBC	EWS	TO (S)	
66134	aosk	WBAE	DBC	EWS	TO	
66135	aosk	WQAA	DBC	DBC	TO (S)	
66136	aoskq	WBAE	DBC	DBC	TO	
66137	aosk	WQAA	DBC	DBC	TO (S)	
66138	aoskq	WBAR	DBC	EWS	TO	
66139	aosk	WBAE	DBC	EWS	TO	
66140	aosk	WBAE	DBC	EWS	TO	
66141	aos	WQDA	DBC	EWS	TO (U)	
66142	aosk	WBAR	DBC	EWS	TO	
66143	aosk	WBAE	DBC	EWS	TO	
66144	aoskq	WBAR	DBC	EWS	TO	
66145	aosk	WBAE	DBC	EWS	TO	
66147	aos	WBAE	DBC	EWS	TO	
66148	aosk	WBAE	DBC	EWS	TO	
66149	aosk	WBAE	DBC	DBC	TO	
66150	aosk	WBAE	DBC	DBC	TO	
66151	aosk	WBAE	DBC	EWS	TO	
66152	aosk	WBAE	DBC	DBS	TO	*Derek Holmes Railway Operator*
66154	aosk	WBAE	DBC	EWS	TO	
66155	aosk	WBAE	DBC	EWS	TO	
66156	aosk	WBAE	DBC	EWS	TO	
66158	aosk	WBAE	DBC	EWS	TO	
66160	aosk	WBAE	DBC	EWS	TO	
66161	aosk	WBAE	DBC	EWS	TO	
66162	aosk	WBAR	DBC	EWS	TO	
66164	aosk	WBAE	DBC	EWS	TO	
66165	aosq	WBAR	DBC	DBC	TO	
66167	aosk	WBAE	DBC	EWS	TO	
66168	aoskq	WBAR	DBC	EWS	TO	
66169	aos	WBAR	DBC	EWS	TO	
66170	aosk	WBAE	DBC	EWS	TO	
66171	aosq	WBAR	DBC	EWS	TO	
66172	aos	WBAE	DBC	EWS	TO	*PAUL MELLANY*
66174	aosk	WBAE	DBC	EWS	TO	
66175	aoskq	WBAE	DBC	DBC	TO	
66176	aoskq	WQAA	DBC	EWS	TO (S)	
66177	aos	WBAT	DBC	EWS	TO	
66181	aoskq	WBAR	DBC	EWS	TO	
66182	aosk	WBAE	DBC	EWS	TO	
66183	aosk	WBAE	DBC	EWS	TO	
66185	aosk	WBAE	DBC	DBS	TO	*DP WORLD London Gateway*
66186	aos	WBAE	DBC	EWS	TO	
66187	aosk	WBAE	DBC	EWS	TO	
66188	aoskq	WQAA	DBC	EWS	TO (S)	
66192	aoskq	WBAR	DBC	DBC	TO	
66194	aoskq	WBAR	DBC	EWS	TO	
66197	aosk	WBAE	DBC	EWS	TO	
66198	aoskq	WBAR	DBC	EWS	TO	
66199	aosk	WBAE	DBC	EWS	TO	
66200	aosk	WQAA	DBC	EWS	TO (S)	
66206	aoskq	WBAR	DBC	DBC	TO	

66207	aosk	WBAE	DBC	EWS	TO
66221	aos	WBAT	DBC	EWS	TO
66230	aosk	WBAE	DBC	EWS	TO (U)

Note: 66003-250 have swinghead couplers
Note: 66136 has YIWU-LONDON TRAIN branding
Note: All DB Cargo Class 66/67s in the WQAA pool are expected to move back to active pools

Class 66/3 – ordered by Fastline Freight

Details as per Class 66/0 except:

Years introduced:	2008
Engine Type:	GM 12N-710G3B-T2
Traction Motor type:	GM-EMD D43TRC
Fuel tank capacity:	1,145gal (5,150lit)

66301	aosr	XHIM	BEA	DRX	KM	*Kingmoor TMD*
66302	aosr	XHIM	BEA	DRX	KM	
66303	aosr	XHIM	BEA	DRX	KM	
66304	aosr	XHIM	BEA	DRX	KM	
66305	aosr	XHIM	BEA	DRX	KM	

Class 66/4 – ordered by DRS

Details as per Class 66/3 except:

| Years introduced: | 2006-08 |

| 66413 | aos | DFIN | MAQ | GWO | LD |
| 66414 | aos | DFIN | MAQ | FPH | LD |

Following the takeover of the Freightliner business by American company Wyoming & Genesee, 66413 became the first loco to be painted in the company's new corporate colours. *Freightliner*

66415	aos	DFIN	MAQ	DRU	LD	
66416	aos	DFIN	MAQ	FPH	LD	
66418	aos	DFIN	MAQ	FPH	LD	*PATRIOT – IN MEMORY OF FALLEN RAILWAY EMPLOYEES*
66419	aos	DFIN	MAQ	DRU	LD	
66420	aos	DFIN	MAQ	FPH	LD	
66421	aos	XHIM	MAQ	DRX	KM	*Gresty Bridge TMD*
66422	aos	XHIM	MAQ	DRX	KM	
66423	aos	XHIM	MAQ	DRX	KM	
66424	aos	XHIM	MAQ	DRX	KM	
66425	aos	XHIM	MAQ	DRX	KM	
66426	aos	XHIM	MAQ	DRX	KM	
66427	aos	XHIM	MAQ	DRX	KM	
66428	aos	XHIM	MAQ	DRX	KM	
66429	aos	XHIM	MAQ	DRX	KM	
66430	aos	XHIM	MAQ	DRX	KM	
66431	aos	XHIM	MAQ	DRX	KM	
66432	aos	XHIM	MAQ	DRX	KM	
66433	aos	XHIM	MAQ	DRX	KM	
66434	aos	XHIM	MAQ	DRX	KM	

Class 66/5 – ordered by Freightliner

Details for 66501-572 as per Class 66/0, details for 66585-599 as per Class 66/3 except:
Years introduced: 1999-2008

66501	aos	DFIM	POR	FLR	LD	*Japan 2001*
66502	aos	DFIM	POR	FLR	LD	*Basford Hall Centenary 2001*
66503	aos	DFIM	POR	FLR	LD	*The RAILWAY MAGAZINE*
66504	aos	DFIM	POR	FPH	LD	
66505	aos	DFIM	POR	FLR	LD	
66506	aos	DFIM	EVS	FLR	LD	*Crewe Regeneration*
66507	aosc	DFHJ	EVS	FLR	LD	
66508	aos	DFIM	EVS	FLR	LD	
66509	aos	DFIM	EVS	FLR	LD	
66510	aos	DFIM	EVS	FLR	LD	
66511	aos	DFIM	EVS	FLR	LD	
66512	aos	DFIM	EVS	FLR	LD	
66513	aos	DFIM	EVS	FLR	LD	
66514	aos	DFIM	EVS	FLR	LD	
66515	aos	DFIM	EVS	FLR	LD	
66516	aos	DFIM	EVS	FLR	LD	
66517	aos	DFIM	EVS	FLR	LD	
66518	aos	DFIM	EVS	FLR	LD	
66519	aos	DFIM	EVS	FLR	LD	
66520	aos	DFIM	EVS	FLR	LD	
66522	aosc	DFHJ	EVS	FLR	LD	
66523	aos	DFIM	EVS	FLR	LD	
66524	aos	DFIM	EVS	FLR	LD	
66525	aos	DFIM	EVS	FLR	LD	
66526	aos	DFIM	EVS	FLR	LD	*Driver Steve Dunn (George)*
66528	aos	DFIM	POR	FPH	LD	*Madge Elliot MBE Borders Railway Opening 2015*
66529	aos	DFIM	POR	FLR	LD	
66531	aos	DFIM	POR	FLR	LD	

66532	aos	DFIM	POR	FLR	LD	P&O Nedlloyd Atlas
66533	aos	DFIM	POR	FLR	LD	Hanjin Express/Senator Express
66534	aos	DFIM	POR	FLR	LD	OOCL Express
66536	aos	DFIM	POR	FLR	LD	
66537	aos	DFIM	POR	FLR	LD	
66538	aos	DFIM	EVS	FLR	LD	
66539	aos	DFIM	EVS	FLR	LD	
66540	aos	DFIM	EVS	FLR	LD	Ruby
66541	aos	DFIM	EVS	FLR	LD	
66542	aos	DFIM	EVS	FLR	LD	
66543	aos	DFIM	EVS	FLR	LD	
66544	aos	DFIM	EVS	FLR	LD	
66545	aos	DFIM	POR	FLR	LD	
66546	aos	DFIM	POR	FLR	LD	
66547	aos	DFIM	POR	FLR	LD	
66548	aos	DFIM	POR	FLR	LD	
66549	aos	DFIM	POR	FLR	LD	
66550	aos	DFIM	POR	FLR	LD	
66551	aos	DFIM	POR	FLR	LD	
66552	aos	DFIM	POR	FLR	LD	Maltby Raider
66553	aos	DFIM	POR	FLR	LD	
66554	aos	DFIM	EVS	FLR	LD	
66555	aos	DFIM	EVS	FLR	LD	
66556	aos	DFIM	EVS	FLR	LD	
66557	aos	DFIM	EVS	FLR	LD	
66558	aos	DFIM	EVS	FLR	LD	
66559	aos	DFIM	EVS	FLR	LD	
66560	aos	DFIM	EVS	FLR	LD	
66561	aos	DFIM	EVS	FLR	LD	
66562	aos	DFIM	EVS	FLR	LD	
66563	aos	DFIM	EVS	FLR	LD	
66564	aos	DFIM	EVS	FLR	LD	
66565	aos	DFIM	EVS	FLR	LD	
66566	aos	DFIM	EVS	FLR	LD	
66567	aos	DFIM	EVS	FLR	LD	
66568	aos	DFIM	EVS	FLR	LD	
66569	aos	DFIM	EVS	FLR	LD	
66570	aos	DFIM	EVS	FLR	LD	
66571	aos	DFIM	EVS	FLR	LD	
66572	aos	DFIM	EVS	FLR	LD	
66585	aos	DFIN	MAQ	FLR	LD	
66587	aos	DFIN	MAQ	FLR	LD	
66588	aos	DFIN	MAQ	FLR	LD	
66589	aos	DFIN	MAQ	FLR	LD	
66590	aos	DFIN	MAQ	FLR	LD	
66591	aos	DFIN	MAQ	FLR	LD	
66592	aos	DFIN	MAQ	FLR	LD	Johnson Stevens Agencies
66593	aos	DFIN	MAQ	FLR	LD	3MG MERSEY MULTIMODAL GATEWAY
66594	aos	DFIN	MAQ	FLR	LD	NYK Spirit of Kyoto
66596	aos	DFIN	BEA	FLR	LD	
66597	aos	DFIN	BEA	FLR	LD	Viridor
66598	aos	DFIN	BEA	FLR	LD	
66599	aos	DFIN	BEA	FLR	LD	

Note: DFHJ locos are expected to move back into the DFIM pool after the RHTT season

Class 66/6 – regeared locos ordered by Freightliner

Details for 66601-622 as per Class 66/0, details for 66623 as per Class 66/3 except:

Years introduced:	2000-07				
Maximum tractive effort:	105,080lbf (467kN)				
Continuous tractive effort:	66,630lbf (296kN)				
Maximum design speed:	65mph (104km/h)				

66601	aos	DFHH	POR	FLR	LD	*The Hope Valley*
66602	aos	DFHH	POR	FLR	LD	
66603	aos	DFHH	POR	FLR	LD	
66604	aos	DFHH	POR	FLR	LD	
66605	aos	DFHH	POR	FLR	LD	
66606	aos	DFHH	POR	FLR	LD	
66607	aos	DFHH	POR	FLR	LD	
66610	aos	DFHH	POR	FLR	LD	
66613	aos	DFHH	EVS	FLR	LD	
66614	aos	DFHH	EVS	FLR	LD	*1916 POPPY 2016*
66615	aos	DFHH	EVS	FLR	LD	
66616	aos	DFHH	EVS	FLR	LD	
66617	aos	DFHH	EVS	FLR	LD	
66618	aos	DFHH	EVS	FLR	LD	*Railways Illustrated Annual Photographic Awards Alan Barnes*
66619	aos	DFHH	EVS	FLR	LD	*Derek W. Johnson MBE*
66620	aos	DFHH	EVS	FLR	LD	
66621	aos	DFHH	EVS	FLR	LD	
66622	aos	DFHH	EVS	FLR	LD	
66623	aos	DFHH	MAQ	BAF	LD	*Bill Bolsover*

Class 66/7 – locos ordered or acquired by GB Railfreight

Details for 66701-751 as per Class 66/0, details for 66752-779 as per Class 66/3 except:

Years introduced:	2001-16
Engine:	EMD 12N-710G3B-T2 (66718-732/747-749)
Traction Motor type:	GM-EMD D43TRC (66718-732/747-749)
Fuel tank capacity:	1,440gal (6,550lit) 66701-717/733-746/750/751, 1,220gal (5,546lit) – 66718-722, 1,312gal (5,150lit) – 66723-732/747-749/752-779

66701	aos	GBBT	EVS	GBO	RR	
66702	aos	GBBT	EVS	GBR	RR	*Blue Lightning*
66703	aos	GBBT	EVS	GBR	RR	*Doncaster PSB 1981-2002*
66704	aos	GBBT	EVS	GBR	RR	*Colchester Power Signalbox*
66705	aos	GBBT	EVS	GBR	RR	*Golden Jubilee*
66706	aos	GBBT	EVS	GBR	RR	*Nene Valley*
66707	aos	GBBT	EVS	GBR	RR	*Sir Sam Fay*
66708	aos	GBBT	EVS	GBR	RR	*Jayne*
66709	aos	GBBT	EVS	MSC	RR	*Sorrento*
66710	aos	GBBT	EVS	GBR	RR	*Phil Packer BRIT*
66711	aos	GBBT	EVS	AGI	RR	*Sence*
66712	aos	GBBT	EVS	GBR	RR	*Peterborough Power Signalbox*
66713	aos	GBBT	EVS	GBR	RR	*Forest City*
66714	aos	GBBT	EVS	GBR	RR	*Cromer Lifeboats*
66715	aos	GBBT	EVS	GBR	RR	*VALOUR*

66716		aos	GBBT	EVS	GBR	RR	*LOCOMOTIVE & CARRIAGE INSTITUTION CENTENARY 1911-2011*
66717		aos	GBBT	EVS	GBR	RR	*Good Old Boy*
66718		aos	GBLT	EVS	LUB	RR	*Sir Peter Hendy CBE*
66719		aos	GBLT	EVS	GBR	RR	*METRO-LAND*
66720		aos	GBLT	EVS	EMY	RR	
66721		aos	GBLT	EVS	LUW	RR	*Harry Beck*
66722		aos	GBLT	EVS	GBR	RR	*Sir Edward Watkin*
66723		aos	GBLT	EVS	GBZ	RR	*Chinook*
66724		aos	GBLT	EVS	GBF	RR	*Drax Power Station*
66725		aos	GBLT	EVS	GBZ	RR	*SUNDERLAND*
66726		aos	GBLT	EVS	GBF	RR	*SHEFFIELD WEDNESDAY*
66727		aos	GBLT	EVS	MRT	RR	*Maritime One*
66728		aos	GBLT	EVS	GBR	RR	*Institution of Railway Operators*
66729		aos	GBLT	EVS	GBR	RR	*DERBY COUNTY*
66730		aos	GBLT	EVS	GBR	RR	*Whitemoor*
66731		aos	GBLT	EVS	GBR	RR	*InterhubGB*
66732		aos	GBLT	EVS	GBR	RR	*GBRF The First Decade 1999-2009 John Smith MD*
66733	66401	aosr	GBFM	POR	GBR	RR	*Cambridge PSB*
66735	66403	aosr	GBBT	POR	GBR	RR	
66736	66404	aosr	GBFM	POR	GBR	RR	*WOLVERHAMPTON WANDERERS*
66737	66405	aosr	GBFM	POR	GBR	RR	*Lesia*
66738	66578	aosr	GBBT	BEA	GBR	RR	*HUDDERSFIELD TOWN*
66739	66579	aos	GBFM	BEA	GBR	RR	*Bluebell Railway*
66740	66580	aosr	GBFM	BEA	GBR	RR	*Sarah*
66741	66581	aos	GBBT	BEA	GBR	RR	*Swanage Railway*
66742	66406, 66841	aos	GBBT	BEA	GBR	RR	*ABP Port of Immingham Centenary 1912-2012*
66743	66407, 66842	aosr	GBFM	BEA	ROY	RR	
66744	66408, 66843	aos	GBBT	BEA	GBR	RR	*Crossrail*
66745	66409, 66844	aos	GBRT	BEA	GBR	RR	*Modern Railways The first 50 years*
66746	66410, 66845	aostr	GBFM	BEA	ROY	RR	
66747		aos	GBEB	GBR	GBR	RR	
66748		aos	GBEB	GBR	GBR	RR	*West Burton 50*
66749		aos	GBEB	GBR	GBR	RR	
66750		aos	GBEB	BEA	GBR	RR	*Bristol Panel Signal Box*
66751		aos	GBEB	BEA	GBR	RR	*Inspirational Delivered Hitachi Rail Europe*
66752		aos	GBEL	GBR	GBR	RR	*The Hoosier State*
66753		aos	GBEL	GBR	GBR	RR	*EMD Roberts Road*
66754		aos	GBEL	GBR	GBR	RR	*Northampton Saints*
66755		aos	GBEL	GBR	GBR	RR	*Tony Berkeley OBE RFG Chairman 1997-2018*
66756		aos	GBEL	GBR	GBR	RR	*Royal Corps of Signals*
66757		aos	GBEL	GBR	GBR	RR	*West Somerset Railway*
66758		aos	GBEL	GBR	GBR	RR	*The Pavior*
66759		aos	GBEL	GBR	GBR	RR	*Chippy*
66760		aos	GBEL	GBR	GBR	RR	*David Gordon Harris*
66761		aos	GBEL	GBR	GBR	RR	*Wensleydale Railway Association 25 Years 1990-2015*
66762		aos	GBEL	GBR	GBR	RR	
66763		aos	GBEL	GBR	GBR	RR	*Severn Valley Railway*

66764		aos	GBEL	GBR	GBR	RR	
66765		aos	GBEL	GBR	GBR	RR	
66766		aos	GBEL	GBR	GBR	RR	
66767		aos	GBEL	GBR	GBR	RR	
66768		aos	GBEL	GBR	GBR	RR	
66769		aos	GBEL	GBR	GBR	RR	
66770		aos	GBEL	GBR	GBR	RR	
66771		aos	GBEL	GBR	GBR	RR	
66772		aos	GBEL	GBR	GBR	RR	
66773		aos	GBNB	GBR	GBR	RR	
66774		aos	GBNB	GBR	GBR	RR	
66775		aos	GBNB	GBR	GBZ	RR	*HMS Argyll*
66776		aos	GBNB	GBR	GBR	RR	*Joanne*
66777		aos	GBNB	GBR	GBR	RR	*Annette*
66778		aos	GBNB	GBR	GBR	RR	*Darius Cheskin*
66779		aos	GBEL	GBR	GYP	RR	*EVENING STAR*
66780	66008	aos	GBOB	GBR	CMX	RR	
66781	66016	aos	GBOB	GBR	GBR	RR	
66782	66046	aos	GBOB	GBR	GBZ	RR	
66783	66058	aosh	GBOB	GBR	BIF	RR	*The Flying Dustman*
66784	66081	aos	GBOB	GBR	GBR	RR	*Keighley & Worth Valley Railway 50th Anniversary 1968-2018*
66785	66132	aos	GBOB	GBR	GBR	RR	
66786	66141	aos	GBOB	GBR	GBR	RR	
66787	66184	aos	GBOB	GBR	GBR	RR	
66788	66238	aos	GBOB	GBR	GBR	RR	
66789	66250	aos	GBOB	GBR	BLL	RR	*British Rail 1948-1997*

Note: 66723 carries ZA723 as well as its TOPS number
Note: 66775 carries F231 as well as its TOPS number

Class 66/8 – locos acquired by Colas Rail Freight
Details as per Class 66/0 except:
Years introduced:	2003/04 (as 66/5s)
Fuel tank capacity:	1,440gal (6,550lit)

66846	66573	aost	COLO	COL	COL	RU	
66847	66574	aost	COLO	COL	COL	RU	
66848	66575	aost	COLO	COL	COL	RU	
66849	66576	aost	COLO	COL	COL	RU	*Wylam Dilly*
66850	66577	aost	COLO	COL	COL	RU	*David Maidment OBE*

Class 66/9 – low emission locos ordered by Freightliner
Details as per Class 66/3 except:
Years introduced:	2004/08
Fuel tank capacity:	1,224gal (5,510lit); t – 1,312gal (5,905lit)

66951	aost	DFIN	EVS	FLR	LD	
66952	aos	DFIN	EVS	FLR	LD	
66953	aos	DFIN	BEA	FLR	LD	
66955	aos	DFIN	BEA	FLR	LD	
66956	aos	DFIN	BEA	FLR	LD	
66957	aos	DFIN	BEA	FLR	LD	*Stephenson Locomotive Society 1909-2009*

GB Railfreight acquired ten Class 66s from DB Cargo in 2017 and renumbered them into its 66/7 series. The last, 66789, the former 66250, was repainted into British Rail 'large logo' livery, a first for a Class 66. Named *British Rail 1948-1997*, it passes Spalding on 26 March 2018 hauling a Middleton Towers-Goole sand train. *Pip Dunn*

Captrains Class 66

This loco is a European Spec Class 66 brought to the UK for repairs at Longport. It was added to TOPS to allow it to be moved on Network Rail infrastructure. It was still in the UK as this book closed for press but should return to the Netherlands when its repairs are completed. Other Class 66s from Europe could visit Longport and these may be added to TOPS.

66999	6601	aos	GROC	HQ

Class 67

Essentially a Bo-Bo, ETH-fitted 125mph mixed traffic version of the Class 66, 30 locos were ordered by EWS and delivered in 1999-2000. Two have since been sold to Colas Rail Freight, but reducing work means several are withdrawn.

Built by:	Alstom/General Motors, Valencia, Spain
Years introduced:	1999-2000
Wheel arrangement:	Bo-Bo
Weight:	90 tons
Length:	64ft 7in (19.71m)
Engine Type:	GM 12N-710G3B-EC
Engine output:	2,980hp (2,223kW)

One of five DB Cargo Class 67s painted in the company's corporate livery, 67015 works Arriva Trains Wales' 1D34, the 0950 Manchester Piccadilly-Holyhead, past Penmaenmawr on 19 April 2018. *Anthony Hicks*

Power at rail	2,493hp (1,860kW)
Maximum tractive effort:	31,750lbf (141kN)
Continuous tractive effort:	20,200lbf (90kN)
ETH index:	66
Maximum design speed:	125mph (200km/h) restricted to 110mph (177km/h)
Brake Force	78 tons
Route Availability:	8
Traction alternator:	GM-EMD AR9A
Companion alternator:	GM-EMD CA6HEX
Traction Motor type:	GM-EMD D43FM
Fuel tank capacity	1,095gal (4,927lit)
Multiple Working type:	AAR

67001	aep	WQAA	DBC	ATW	TO (S)	
67002	aep	WAAC	DBC	ATW	CE	
67003	aep	WAAC	DBC	ATW	CE	
67004	aepr	WABC	DBC	DBC	TO	
67005	aep	WAAC	DBC	RTO	CE	*Queen's Messenger*
67006	aep	WAAC	DBC	RTO	CE	*Royal Sovereign*
67007	aepr	WQAA	DBC	EWS	CE (S)	
67008	aep	WQAA	DBC	EWS	CE (S)	
67009	aepr	WQAA	DBC	EWS	CE (S)	
67010	aep	WAAC	DBC	DBC	CE	

67011	aepr	WQAB	DBC	EWS	CE (S)	
67012	aep	WAAC	DBC	CRS	CE	
67013	aep	WAWC	DBC	DBC	CE	
67014	aep	WAAC	DBC	CRS	CE	
67015	aep	WAAC	DBC	CRS	CE	
67016	aep	WAAC	DBC	EWS	CE	
67017	aep	WQAB	DBC	EWS	CE (S)	*Arrow*
67018	aep	WAAC	DBC	DBS	CE	*Keith Heller*
67019	aep	WQBA	DBC	EWS	TO (U)	
67020	aep	WAWC	DBC	EWS	CE	
67021	aep	WAAC	DBC	PUL	CE	
67022	aep	WAAC	DBC	EWS	CE	
67023	aep	COTS	COL	COL	RU	*Charlotte*
67024	aep	WAAC	DBC	PUL	CE	
67025	aep	WQBA	DBC	EWS	CE (U)	*Western Star*
67026	aep	WQAB	DBC	JUB	CE (S)	*Diamond Jubilee*
67027	aep	COTS	COL	COL	RU	*Stella*
67028	aep	WAAC	DBC	DBC	CE	
67029	aepq	WAWC	DBC	DBM	CE	*Royal Diamond*
67030	aepr	WABC	DBC	EWS	CE	

Note: 67010 has 'First choice for rail freight in the UK' branding
Note: 67028 has 'Leading the next generation of rail freight' branding
Note: 67001-030 have swinghead couplers

Class 68

New mixed traffic Bo-Bo loco ordered by DRS in 2012. Initial order for 15 upped to 25, then 32 and presently 34 locos. More could be ordered. 68019-032 will be dedicated for Transpennine use (these are currently being modified and re-liveried), while 68010-015 are dedicated to Chiltern Railways services.

Built by:	Vossloh/Stadler, Valencia
Years introduced:	2014-17
Wheel arrangement:	Bo-Bo
Weight:	85 tons
Length:	20.5m
Engine Type:	Caterpillar C175-16
Engine output:	3,805hp (2,839kW)
Power at rail:	3,190hp (2,380kW)
Tractive effort:	71,260lbf (317kN)
Continuous tractive effort	56,200lbf (250kN)
ETH index:	96
Maximum design speed:	100mph (160km/h)
Brake Force:	73 tons
Route Availability:	7
Main alternator type:	ABB WGX560
Traction Motor type:	ABB 4FRA6063
Fuel tank capacity:	1,120gal (5,600lit)
Multiple Working type:	within class and Class 88 only

68001	aep*	XHVE	BEA	DRN	CR	*Evolution*
68002	aep*	XHVE	BEA	DRN	CR	*Intrepid*
68003	aep*	XHVE	BEA	DRN	CR	*Astute*
68004	aep*	XHVE	BEA	DRN	CR	*Rapid*

Direct Rail Services' 68002 *Intrepid* leads 68026 on 6K41, the 1458 Valley-Crewe nuclear flask train, past Llanfairyneubwll just a few miles into its journey on 20 April 2018. The latter loco has since lost its plain DRS blue livery for Transpennine Express colours. *Anthony Hicks*

One of two DRS Class 68s in ScotRail colours, 68006 *Daring* pauses at Haymarket on 24 July 2018 while working the 1718 Edinburgh-Glenrothes. *Pip Dunn*

68005	aep*	XHVE	BEA	DRN	CR	*Defiant*
68006	aep*	XHVE	BEA	SCR	CR	*Daring*
68007	aep*	XHVE	BEA	SCR	CR	*Valiant*
68008	aeup*	XHVE	BEA	DRN	CR	*Avenger*
68009	aeup*	XHVE	BEA	DRN	CR	*Titan*
68010	aeup*	XHCE	BEA	CRS	CR	*Oxford Flyer*
68011	aeup*	XHCE	BEA	CRS	CR	
68012	aeup*	XHCE	BEA	CRS	CR	
68013	aeup*	XHCE	BEA	CRS	CR	
68014	aeup*	XHCE	BEA	CRS	CR	
68015	aeup*	XHCE	BEA	CRS	CR	
68016	aep*	XHVE	BEA	DRN	CR	*Fearless*
68017	aep*	XHVE	BEA	DRN	CR	*Hornet*
68018	aep*	XHVE	BEA	DRN	CR	*Vigilant*
68019	aeup*	XHTP	BEA	TPE	CR	*Brutus*
68020	aeup*	XHTP	BEA	DRU	CR	*Reliance*
68021	aeup*	XHTP	BEA	TPE	CR	*Tireless*
68022	aeup*	XHTP	BEA	DRU	CR	*Resolution*
68023	aeup*	XHTP	BEA	TPE	CR	*Achilles*
68024	aeup*	XHTP	BEA	TPE	BH	*Centaur*
68025	aeup*	XHTP	BEA	DRN	CR	*Superb*
68026	aeup*	XHTP	BEA	TPE	CR	
68027	aeup*	XHTP	BEA	DRX	CR	
68028	aeup*	XHTP	BEA	TPE	CR	*Lord President*
68029	aeup*	XHTP	BEA	TPE	CR	
68030	aeup*	XHTP	BEA	DRX	CR	
68031	aeup*	XHTP	BEA	DRX	CR	
68032	aeup*	XHTP	BEA	TPE	CR	
68033	aep*	XHVE	BEA	DRN	CR	
68034	aep*	XHVE	BEA	DRN	CR	

Note: XHVE/XHCE and XHTP locos have different push-pull systems and are not interoperable between the pools

Class 70

General Electric freight loco design ordered by Freightliner. The initial order was for 20 locos with an option for ten more, which was not taken up. Instead those locos were taken by Colas Rail Freight, which later ordered seven more.

Freightliner's 70012 was delivered to the UK but badly damaged when it was dropped by the crane during unloading, so it was returned to the USA and is deemed as disposed.

70801 was formerly a demonstrator loco numbered 70099 that was built from a kit delivered to Turkey and shipped to the UK before being taken on by Colas.

Built by:	General Electric, Erie, Pennsylvania
Years introduced:	2009-12
Wheel arrangement:	Co-Co
Weight:	129 tons
Length:	21.71m
Engine Type:	GE Powerhaul P616LDA1
Engine output:	3,820hp (2,848kW)
Power at rail:	2,700hp (2,014kW)
Tractive effort:	122,000lbf (544kN)
Continuous tractive effort	96,000lbf (427kN)
Maximum design speed:	75mph (120km/h)

Freightliner's Class 70s have not been a glowing success, and several have been stored for some time now. 70019 passes Acton Turville, near Chipping Sodbury, on 18 July 2013 while hauling 4V50, the 1032 Millbrook-Wentloog intermodal train. *Martin Loader*

Brake Force:	96.7 tons
Route Availability:	7
Main alternator type:	GE 5GTAZ6721A1
Traction Motor type:	AC-GE 5GEB30B
Fuel tank capacity:	1,333gal (6,000lit)
Multiple Working type:	AAR

Class 70/0 – Freightliner Locos

70001	aos	DHLT	MAQ	FPH	LD (U)	*PowerHaul*
70002	aos	DHLT	MAQ	FPH	LD	
70003	aos	DFGI	MAQ	FPH	LD	
70004	aos	DHLT	MAQ	FPH	LD (U)	*The Coal Industry Society*
70005	aos	DFGI	MAQ	FPH	LD	
70006	aos	DHLT	MAQ	FPH	LD (U)	
70007	aos	DFGI	MAQ	FPH	LD	
70008	aos	DFGI	MAQ	FPH	LD	
70009	aos	DHLT	MAQ	FPH	LD (U)	
70010	aos	DHLT	MAQ	FPH	LD (U)	
70011	aos	DHLT	MAQ	FPH	LD	
70013	aos	DHLT	MAQ	FPH	LD (U)	
70014	aos	DFGI	MAQ	FPH	LD	
70015	aos	DHLT	MAQ	FPH	LD	
70016	aos	DHLT	MAQ	FPH	LD (U)	
70017	aos	DHLT	MAQ	FPH	LD (U)	
70018	aos	DHLT	MAQ	FPH	LD (U)	
70019	aos	DHLT	MAQ	FPH	LD (U)	
70020	aos	DFGI	MAQ	FPH	LD	

One of 17 Class 70/8s in traffic with Colas Rail Freight, 70812 leads 6C80, the 1841 Doncaster-Haywood Junction infrastructure train, past Burton Salmon on 28 July 2018. *Anthony Hicks*

Class 70/8 – Colas Rail Freight locos
Details as per Class 70/0

70801	70099	aos	COLO	LOM	COL	CF
70802		aos	COLO	LOM	COL	CF
70803		aos	COLO	LOM	COL	CF
70804		aos	COLO	LOM	COL	CF
70805		aos	COLO	LOM	COL	CF
70806		aos	COLO	LOM	COL	CF
70807		aos	COLO	LOM	COL	CF
70808		aos	COLO	LOM	COL	CF
70809		aos	COLO	LOM	COL	CF
70810		aos	COLO	LOM	COL	CF
70811		aos	COLO	LOM	COL	CF
70812		aos	COLO	LOM	COL	CF
70813		aos	COLO	LOM	COL	CF
70814		aos	COLO	LOM	COL	CF
70815		aos	COLO	LOM	COL	CF
70816		aos	COLO	LOM	COL	CF
70817		aos	COLO	LOM	COL	CF

Class 73
A fleet of six prototype Electro Diesel locos (Class 73/0) was built in 1962 by BR at Eastleigh followed by a production series of 43 locos (Class 73/1) built by EE at Vulcan Foundry in 1965. In 1988, 12, later increased to 14, locos were modified for dedicated Gatwick Express use (Class 73/2), while two 73/0s were converted for Sandite use on Merseyrail as Class 73/9s.

Two re-engineering progammes have recently been undertaken, one by RVEL (now LORAM) at Derby for Network Rail that saw the EE diesel engine replaced by two Cummins engines. Only two locos have been modified and no more conversions are expected.

Brush also rebuilt 11 locos for GBRf with single MTU engines. Five of these are for NR contacts (73961-965) while the other six (73966-971) are dedicated for Caledonian Sleeper work in Scotland. There are a few differences between these two fleets. More GBRf conversions may be forthcoming and the company still retains a sizeable fleet of original 73s still in main line use, recently adding three further locos to its stored fleet.

Built by:	English Electric, Vulcan Foundry
Years introduced:	1962-67
Wheel arrangement:	Bo-Bo
Weight:	76-77 tons
Length:	53ft 8in (16.96m)
Power supply:	750V DC third rail
Engine Type:	English Electric 4SRKT Mk 2
Engine output:	600hp (447kW)
Electric output:	1,600hp (1,193kW)
Power at rail (diesel):	402hp (300kW)
Electric power at rail (Cont):	1,200hp (895kW)
Electric power at rail (Max):	2,450hp (1,830kW)
Electric tractive effort:	40,000lb (179kN) – Electric
Diesel tractive effort:	36,000lbf (160kN) – Diesel
Continuous tractive effort	13,600lbf (60kN) – Diesel
ETH index:	38 on electric power only
Maximum design speed:	90mph (144km/h)
Brake Force:	31 tons
Route Availability:	6
Main generator type:	EE824-3D
Auxiliary generator type:	EE908-3C
Traction Motor type:	EE546-1B
Fuel tank capacity:	310gal (1,409lit)
Multiple Working type:	Blue Star

Class 73/1: standard locos

73101	E6007, 73801	xew	GBEB	GBR	PUL	ZG (U)	
73107	E6013	xew	GBED	GBR	GBR	SE	Tracy
73109	E6015	xew	GBED	GBR	GBR	SE	
73110	E6016	xew		GBR	EBY	ZG (U)	
73119	E6025	xew	GBED	GBR	GBR	SE	Borough of Eastleigh
73128	E6035	xew	GBED	GBR	GBR	SE	OVS BULLEID CBE
73134	E6041	xew	GBBR	GBR	ICO	BL (U)	
73136	E6043	xew	GBED	GBR	GBR	SE	Mhairi
73138	E6045	aew	QADD	NET	NRY	SE	
73139	E6046	xew	GBED	GBR	UND	ZG (U)	
73141	E6048	xew	GBED	GBR	GBR	SE	Charlotte
73201	E6049, 73142	aew	GBED	GBR	BRB	SE	Broadlands
73202	E6044, 73137	aew	MBED	POR	SOU	SL	Graham Stenning
73212	E6008, 73102	aewp*	GBED	GBR	GBR	SE	Fiona
73213	E6018, 73112	aewp*	GBED	GBR	GBR	SE	Rhodalyn
73235	E6042, 73135	aew	HYWD	POR	SWU	BM	

Note: 73212/213 have snowplough brackets at one end only

Brightening up a dull afternoon at Bewdley on 19 May 2016, Network Rail's 73952 *Janis Kong* and 73951 *Malcolm Brinded*, work the 1501 Kidderminster-Bewdley. No more conversions of 73/1s with Cummins engines by LORAM are expected to be undertaken. *Martin Loader*

Class 73/9 – LORAM rebuilt locos

Details as per Class 73/1 except:

Built by:	LORAM
Years introduced:	2015
Engine type	two Cummins QSK19
Engine output (total):	1,500hp (1,119kW)
Power at rail (diesel):	1,005hp (750kW)
Electric tractive effort:	40,000lbf (179kN)
Diesel tractive effort:	40,000lbf (179kN)
Maximum design speed:	90mph
Brake Force:	31 tonnes
Fuel tank capacity:	500gal (2,260lit)
Multiple Working type:	AAR

73951	E6010, 73104	ao	QADD	NET	NRY	ZA	*Malcolm Brinded*
73952	E6019, 73113, 73211	ao	QADD	NET	NRY	ZA	*Janis Kong*

Class 73/9 – Brush rebuilt locos

Details as per Class 73/1 except:

Built by:	Brush Loughborough
Years introduced:	2014-15
Engine type	MTU R4000L 8V43
Engine output:	1,600hp (1,194kW)

Six of the 11 Class 73s rebuilt by Brush with MTU engines as Class 73/9s for GB Railfreight are dedicated for use on Caledonian Sleeper trains. 73969 waits to leave with 1B16, the 2143 Aberdeen-Edinburgh, on 14 March 2018. *Anthony Hicks*

Power at rail (diesel):	1,072hp (800kW)
ETH index:	50 (73961-965), 90 (73966-971)
Maximum design speed:	90mph
Brake Force:	31 tonnes
Main alternator type:	Lechmotoren SDV 87.53-12
Multiple Working type:	Blue Star and AAR

73961	E6026, 73120, 73209	aetwp	GBNR	GBR	GBR	SE	*Alison*
73962	E6032, 73125, 73204	aetwp	GBNR	GBR	GBR	SE	*Dick Mabbutt*
73963	E6030, 73123, 73206	aetwp	GBNR	GBR	GBR	SE	*Janice*
73964	E6031, 73124, 73205	aetwp	GBNR	GBR	GBR	SE	*Jeanette*
73965	E6028, 73121, 73208	aetwp	GBNR	GBR	GBR	SE	
73966	E6005, 73005	aetrdp*	GBCS	GBR	CAL	EC	
73967	E6006, 73006, 73906	aetrdp*	GBCS	GBR	CAL	EC	
73968	E6023, 73117	aetrdp*	GBCS	GBR	CAL	EC	
73969	E6011, 73105	aetrdp*	GBCS	GBR	CAL	EC	
73970	E6009, 73103	aetrdp*	GBCS	GBR	CAL	EC	
73971	E6029, 73122, 73207	aetrdp*	GBCS	GBR	CAL	EC	

Note: 73962/964 have cab end brackets for fitting ladders for working on the East London Line
The 750V DC capability on 73966-971 is currently isolated

Class 86

The standard 25kV AC loco built for BR in the mid-1960s, totalling 100 examples. Sixty-one were modified to Class 86/2s, while the remaining Class 86/0s were later changed to either Class 86/3s or 86/4s, with the 86/3s duly becoming 86/4s. Of the 39 Class 86/4s, 30 were converted to freight only Class 86/6s, 16 of which remain in traffic with Freightliner.

Several Class 86/2s have been exported for use in Bulgaria and Hungary.

Built by:	English Electric Vulcan Foundry and BR Doncaster
Years introduced:	1965-66
Wheel arrangement:	Bo-Bo
Weight:	83-87 tons
Length:	58ft 6in (17.83m)
Power supply	25kV AC
Control system:	HT tap changing
Traction output (max):	7,680hp (5,860kW)
Traction output (cont.):	5,000hp (3,730kW)
Tractive effort:	58,000lb (258kN)
ETH index:	74
Maximum design speed:	100-110mph (160-180km/h)
Brake Force:	40 tons
Route Availability:	6
Traction Motor type:	GEC G412AZ
Multiple Working type:	TDM

Class 86/1 – test locos

86101	E3191, 86201	xe	GBCH	ACL	CAL	WN	*Sir William A Stanier FRS*

Class 86/2 – standard locos

Details as per Class 86/1 except:

Traction output (max):	6,100hp (4,550kW)
Traction output (cont.):	4,040hp (3,013kW)
Traction Motor type:	AEI 282AZ

86259	E3137, 86045	xe	MBEL	LES	EBY	WN	*Les Ross/Peter Pan*

Class 86/4 – regeared locos

Details as per Class 86/1 except:

Traction output (max):	5,900hp (4,400kW)
Traction output (cont.):	3,600hp (2,680kW)
Traction Motor type:	AEI 282AZ

86401	E3199, 86001	xe	GBCH	ACL	CAL	WN	*Mons Meg*

Class 86/6 – freight only locos

Details as per Class 86/1 except:

Traction output (max):	5,900hp (4,400kW)
Traction output (cont.):	3,600hp (2,680kW)
Maximum design speed:	75mph (120km/h)
Traction Motor type:	AEI 282AZ
No train heating	

On 12 January 2018, Freightliner Intermodal's 86627/638 pause at Ipswich just before running in to the adjacent yard and being swapped for diesel power for the last few miles to Felixstowe. *Al Pulford*

86604	E3103, 86004, 86404	aym	DFNC	FLI	FLH	CB
86605	E3185, 86005, 86405	aym	DFNC	FLI	FLH	CB
86607	E3176, 86007, 86407	aym	DFNC	FLI	FLH	CB
86608	E3180, 86008, 86408, 86501	aym	DFNC	FLI	FLH	CB
86609	E3102, 86009, 86409	aym	DFNC	FLI	FLH	CB
86610	E3104, 86010, 86410	aym	DFNC	FLI	FLH	CB
86612	E3122, 86012, 86312, 86412	aym	DFNC	POR	FLH	CB
86613	E3128, 86013, 86313, 86413	aym	DFNC	POR	FLH	CB
86614	E3145, 86014, 86314, 86414	aym	DFNC	POR	FLH	CB
86622	E3174, 86022, 86322, 86422	aym	DFNC	POR	FPH	CB
86627	E3110, 86027, 86327, 86427	aym	DFNC	POR	FLH	CB
86628	E3159, 86028, 86328, 86428	aym	DFNC	POR	FLH	CB
86632	E3148, 86032, 86432	aym	DFNC	POR	FLH	CB
86637	E3130, 86037, 86437	aym	DFNC	POR	FPH	CB
86638	E3108, 86038, 86438	aym	DFNC	POR	FLH	CB
86639	E3153, 86039, 86439	aym	DFNC	POR	FLH	CB

Class 87

An improved version of the Class 86, 36 locos were built from 1973 for the newly electrified northern section of the WCML. The last of the class were withdrawn by Virgin Trains in the early 2000s. Several have been exported to Bulgaria. One loco remains UK main line registered, on spot hire to GBRf.

Built by:	BREL Crewe
Years introduced:	1973-74
Wheel arrangement:	Bo-Bo
Weight:	83 tons
Length:	58ft 6in (17.83m)
Power supply:	25kV AC
Control system:	HT tap changing
Traction output (max)	7,680hp (5,860kW)
Traction output (Con):	5,000hp (3,730kW)
Tractive effort:	58,000lb
ETH index:	95
Maximum design speed:	110mph (176km/h)
Brake Force:	40 tons
Route Availability:	6
Traction Motor type:	GEC G412AZ
Multiple Working type:	TDM

87002		ae	GBCH	ACL	CAL	WN	*Royal Sovereign*

Class 88 Electro Diesel

An Electro Diesel version of the Class 68 ordered for DRS. They are used mostly for intermodal trains on the West Coast Main Line. Further orders are possible.

Built by:	Vossloh/Stadler, Valencia
Years introduced:	2015
Wheel arrangement:	Bo-Bo
Weight:	85 tons
Length:	20.5m
Power supply:	25kV AC
Engine Type:	Caterpillar C27 12-cylinder
Engine output:	950hp (708kW)
Traction output (Con):	5,360hp (4,000kW)
Tractive effort:	71,260lbf (317kN)
ETH index:	96
Maximum design speed:	100mph (160km/h)
Brake Force:	88 tons
Route Availability:	7
Main alternator type:	ABB AMXL400
Traction Motor type:	ABB AMXL400
Fuel tank capacity:	400gal (1,800lit)
Multiple Working type:	Within Class and Class 68 only

88001		aeup*	XHVE	BEA	DRE	CR	*Revolution*
88002		aeup*	XHVE	BEA	DRE	CR	*Prometheus*
88003		aeup*	XHVE	BEA	DRE	CR	*Genesis*

88002 *Prometheus* and 68025 *Superb* head 1Z39, the 0639 Didcot Parkway-Appleby charter, into its destination on 20 May 2017. The Electro-Diesel Class 88 was working on its auxiliary diesel engine but in multiple with the 68. *Anthony Hicks*

88004	aeup*	XHVE	BEA	DRE	CR	*Pandora*
88005	aeup*	XHVE	BEA	DRE	CR	*Minerva*
88006	aeup*	XHVE	BEA	DRE	CR	*Juno*
88007	aeup*	XHVE	BEA	DRE	CR	*Electra*
88008	aeup*	XHVE	BEA	DRE	CR	*Ariadne*
88009	aeup*	XHVE	BEA	DRE	CR	*Diana*
88010	aeup*	XHVE	BEA	DRE	CR	*Aurora*

Class 90

An enhanced version of the Class 87 – the 90s were originally going to be Class 87/2s. Fifteen locos remain in passenger use with Greater Anglia but will be replaced in 2018/19. The remainder are in freight use with Freightliner and DB Cargo, but withdrawals started over a decade ago.

Built by:	BREL Crewe
Years introduced:	1987-90
Wheel arrangement:	Bo-Bo
Weight:	84.5 tons
Length:	61ft 6in (18.74m)
Power supply:	25kV AC
Control system:	Thyristor
Traction output (max):	7,680hp (5,860kW)
Traction output (con):	5,000hp (3,730kW)
Tractive effort:	58,000lb
ETH index:	95
Maximum design speed:	110mph (176km/h)
Brake Force:	40 tons
Route Availability:	7
Traction Motor type:	GEC G412CY
Multiple Working type:	TDM

90001		aeu	IANA	POR	AGA	NC	Crown Point
90002		aeu	IANA	POR	AGA	NC	Eastern Daily Press 1870-2010 SERVING NORFOLK FOR 140 YEARS
90003		aeu	IANA	POR	AGA	NC	
90004		aeu	IANA	POR	AGA	NC	City of Chelmsford
90005		aeu	IANA	POR	AGA	NC	Vice-Admiral Lord Nelson
90006		aeu	IANA	POR	AGA	NC	Roger Ford/Modern Railways Magazine
90007		aeu	IANA	POR	AGA	NC	Sir John Betjeman
90008		aeu	IANA	POR	AGA	NC	The East Anglian
90009		aeu	IANA	POR	AGA	NC	
90010		aeu	IANA	POR	AGA	NC	
90011		aeu	IANA	POR	AGA	NC	East Anglian Daily Times – Suffolk & Proud
90012		aeu	IANA	POR	AGA	NC	Royal Anglian Regiment
90013		aeu	IANA	POR	AGA	NC	
90014		aeu	IANA	POR	AGA	NC	Norfolk & Norwich Festival
90015		aeu	IANA	POR	AGA	NC	Colchester Castle
90016		aeu	DFLC	POR	FLR	CB	
90017		aeu	WQBA	DBC	EWS	CE (U)	
90018		aeu	WEDC	DBC	DBS	CE	Pride of Bellshill
90019		aeu	WEDC	DBC	DBC	CE	Multimodal
90020		aeu	WEDC	DBC	EWS	CE	Collingwood
90021	90221	aeu	WQAB	DBC	FSR	CE (U)	

90041/044 work the 1213 Daventry-Coatbridge Freightliner Intermodal train past Abington near Carstairs in the Scottish Borders on 19 July 2018. *Anthony Hicks*

90022	90222	aeu	WQBA	DBC	REW	CE (U)	*Freightconnection*
90023	90223	aeu	WQBA	DBC	RFE	CE (U)	
90024	90224	aeu	WEAC	DBC	MAA	CE	
90025	90125, 90225	aeu	WQBA	DBC	RFD	CE (U)	
90026	90126	aeu	WQAB	DBC	EWS	CE (U)	
90027	90127, 90227	aeu	WQBA	DBC	RFD	CE (U)	*Allerton T&RS Depot*
90028	90128	aeu	WEDC	DBC	EWS	CE	
90029	90129	aeu	WEDC	DBC	DBC	CE	
90030	90130	aeu	WQBA	DBC	EWS	CE (U)	
90031	90131	aeu	WQBA	DBC	EWS	CE (U)	*The Railway Children Partnership: Working for Street Children Worldwide*
90032	90132	aeu	WQBA	DBC	EWS	CE (U)	
90033	90133, 90233	aeu	WQBA	DBC	RFE	CE (U)	
90034	90134	aeu	WEDC	DBC	DRU	CE	
90035	90135	aeu	WEAC	DBC	EWS	CE	
90036	90136	aeu	WEDC	DBC	DBC	CE	*Driver Jack Mills*
90037	90137	aeu	WEAC	DBC	EWS	CE	*Spirit of Dagenham*
90038	90138, 90238	aeu	WQBA	DBC	RFE	CE (U)	
90039	90139, 90239	aeu	WEDC	DBC	EWS	CE	
90040	90140	aeu	WEAC	DBC	DBC	CE	
90041	90141	aeu	DFLC	POR	FLR	CB	
90042	90142	aeu	DFLC	POR	FPH	CB	
90043	90143	aeu	DFLC	POR	FPH	CB	
90044	90144	aeu	DFLC	POR	FLG	CB	
90045	90145	aeu	DFLC	POR	FPH	CB	
90046	90146	aeu	DFLC	POR	FLR	CB	
90047	90147	aeu	DFLC	POR	FLG	CB	
90048	90148	aeu	DFLC	POR	FLG	CB	
90049	90149	aeu	DFLC	POR	FPH	CB	
90050	90150	aeu	DHLT	ARV	TTG	CB (U)	

Class 91

Dedicated express passenger locos for the East Coast Main Line, they are to be replaced by new IEP EMUs from 2018 and withdrawals or redeployment will then be inevitable. All were built as 91/0s but refurbished in 2001-03 and renumbered in the 91/1 series.

Built by:	BREL Crewe
Years introduced:	1988-91
Wheel arrangement:	Bo-Bo
Weight:	84 tons
Length:	63ft 8in (19.40m)
Power supply:	25kV AC
Control system:	Thyristor
Traction output (max):	6,300hp (4,700kW)
Traction output (con):	6,090hp (4,540kW)
ETH index:	95
Maximum operating speed:	125mph (200km/h) restricted to 110mph (176km/h) when flat end leading
Brake Force:	45 tons
Route Availability:	7
Traction Motor type:	GEC G426AZ
Multiple Working type:	TDM

On 14 April 2018, 91110 *Battle of Britain Memorial Flight* stands at Leeds having arrived with the 0903 from King's Cross. *Pip Dunn*

91101	91001	aeu	IECA	EVS	VFS	BN	FLYING SCOTSMAN
91102	91002	aeu	IECA	EVS	VEC	BN	City of York
91103	91003	aeu	IECA	EVS	VEA	BN	
91104	91004	aeu	IECA	EVS	VEC	BN	
91105	91005	aeu	IECA	EVS	VEC	BN	
91106	91006	aeu	IECA	EVS	VEA	BN	
91107	91007	aeu	IECA	EVS	VEC	BN	SKYFALL
91108	91008	aeu	IECA	EVS	VEC	BN	
91109	91009	aeu	IECA	EVS	VEC	BN	Sir Bobby Robson
91110	91010	aeu	IECA	EVS	BBM	BN	BATTLE OF BRITAIN MEMORIAL FLIGHT
91111	91011	aeu	IECA	EVS	FTF	BN	For the Fallen
91112	91012	aeu	IECA	EVS	VEC	BN	
91113	91013	aeu	IECA	EVS	VEC	BN	
91114	91014	aeu	IECA	EVS	VEA	BN	Durham Cathedral
91115	91015	aeu	IECA	EVS	VEC	BN	Blaydon Races
91116	91016	aeu	IECA	EVS	VEC	BN	
91117	91017	aeu	IECA	EVS	VEC	BN	WEST RIDING LIMITED
91118	91018	aeu	IECA	EVS	VEC	BN	The Fusiliers
91119	91019	aeu	IECA	EVS	VEC	BN	Bounds Green INTERCITY Depot 1977-2017
91120	91020	aeu	IECA	EVS	VEC	BN	
91121	91021	aeu	IECA	EVS	VEC	BN	
91122	91022	aeu	IECA	EVS	VEC	BN	
91124	91024	aeu	IECA	EVS	VEC	BN	
91125	91025	aeu	IECA	EVS	VEC	BN	
91126	91026	aeu	IECA	EVS	VEC	BN	Darlington Hippodrome
91127	91027	aeu	IECA	EVS	VEC	BN	
91128	91028	aeu	IECA	EVS	VEC	BN	INTERCITY 50

91129	91029	aeu	IECA	EVS	VEC	BN	
91130	91030	aeu	IECA	EVS	VEC	BN	*Lord Mayor of Newcastle*
91131	91031	aeu	IECA	EVS	VEC	BN	
91132	91023	aeu	IECA	EVS	VEA	BN	

Note: 91103 has Celebrating Pride graphics
Note: 91106 has Great Exhibition of the North graphics
Note: 91114 has Durham Cathedral graphics
Note: 91132 has 'time to change Employer Pledge' branding

Class 92

A fleet of 46 locos were ordered for Channel Tunnel work, but much of the traffic never materialised and the locos were woefully underutilised and many withdrawn from 2001.

Seven were owned by Eurostar, nine by SNCF and 30 by BR's Railfreight Distribution sector. The latter all transferred to EWS, while GBRf has bought the other 16. Several DB Cargo locos are now in Bulgaria and Romania.

Two withdrawn locos are expected to be revived and overhauled for GBRf, but disposal of the remaining four is possible.

Built by:	Brush Traction
Years introduced:	1993-95
Wheel arrangement:	Co-Co
Weight:	126 tons
Length:	70ft 1in (21.34m)
Power supply:	25kV AC or 750V DC
Control system:	Asynchronous 3-phase
Traction output (max):	6,700hp (5,000kW) – overhead power supply
	5,360hp (4,000kW) – third rail power supply
Tractive effort:	Normal – 81,000lbf; boost – 90,000lbf
ETH index:	108
Maximum design speed:	87mph (139km/h)
Brake Force:	63 tons
Route Availability:	8
Traction Motor type:	Brush
Multiple working type:	not fitted

92004	ae	WQBA	DBC	EUE	CE (U)	*Jane Austen*
92006	ae	GBET	GBR	EUE	BL (U)	*Louis Armand*
92007	ae	WQBA	DBC	EUK	CE (U)	*Schubert*
92008	ae	WQBA	DBC	EUE	CE (U)	*Jules Verne*
92009	ae	WQBA	DBC	DBC	CE (U)	*Elgar*
92010	ae	GBST	GBR	CAL	WN	
92011	ae	WFBC	DBC	EUE	CE	*Handel*
92013	ae	WQAB	DBC	EUE	CE (U)	*Puccini*
92014	aed	GBSL	GBR	CAL	WN	
92015	ae	WFBC	DBC	DBC	CE	
92016	ae	WQAA	DBC	DBC	CE (U)	
92017	ae	WQBA	DBC	STO	CE (U)	*Bart the Engine*
92018	aed	GBST	GBR	CAL	WN	
92019	ae	WFBC	DBC	EUE	CE	*Wagner*
92020	ae	GBET	GBR	EUK	BL (U)	*Milton*
92021	ae	GBET	GBR	EUK	CO (U)	*Purcell*
92023	ae	GBSL	GBR	CAL	WN	
92028	aed	GBST	GBR	GBR	WN	

GB Railfreight owns 16 Class 92s, ten of which are on traffic, two are being overhauled and four are withdrawn. They are used for Caledonian Sleeper trains south of Edinburgh and 92023 rests in between turns at Waverley on 24 July 2018. *Pip Dunn*

92029	ae	WQBA	DBC	EUE	CE (U)	*Dante*
92031	ae	WQAB	DBC	DBC	CE (U)	*The Institute of Logistics & Transport*
92032	ae	GBST	GBR	GBR	WN	*IMechE Railway Division*
92033	aed	GBSL	GBR	CAL	WN	
92035	ae	WQBA	DBC	EUE	CE (U)	*Mendelssohn*
92036	ae	WFBC	DBC	EUE	CE	*Bertolt Brecht*
92037	ae	WQAB	DBC	EUE	CE (U)	*Sullivan*
92038	aed	GBST	GBR	CAL	WN	
92040	ae	GBET	GBR	EUK	CO (U)	*Goethe*
92041	ae	WFBC	DBC	EUE	CE	*Vaughan Williams*
92042	ae	WFBC	DBC	DBC	CE	
92043	aed	GBST	GBR	GBR	WN	
92044	ae	GBST	GBR	EUK	WN	*Couperin*
92045	ae	GBET	GBR	EUK	BL (U)	*Chaucer*
92046	ae	GBET	GBR	EUK	BL (U)	*Sweelinck*

Note: 92009-011/015/016/018/019/023/031/032/036/038/041-043 have TVM430 in-cab signalling equipment fitted for working on HS1 lines
92006/020 are being overhauled and will return to traffic

2 Spot hire and industrial locos

This section lists all locos regarded as available for short term or medium term spot hire but do not have full main line registration, plus locos that have been sold or moved abroad on a long-term basis. Not all locos are necessarily in operation and some may be disposed of.

Loco's current TOPS number	Previous official numbers carried	Key detail differences	Current TOPS Sector	Vehicle Owner	Current Livery	Current depot allocation or location	Current name (as displayed on the loco) Minor wording on crests, plaques or graphics is excluded

Class 03

03084	D2084	xow		CRB	GWS	CS	
03196	D2196	xow		WCR	BRW	CS (U)	
	D2381	vo		WCR	GNY	CS (U)	

Class 07

07007	D2991	vo	MBDL	AFS	BRW	ZG	
07011	D2995	xow		SLE	BRW	SE	

Class 08

08021	D3029, 13029	vo		TLW	BLK	TM	
08168	D3236, 13236	vo		NEM	BLK	EOR	
08220	D3290, 13290	vo		EEG	BRW	ZW	
08296	D3955, 08787	xo		AGI	BLE	MQ (U)	
08308	D3378	ao	MRSO	RMS	FSR	PD	
08375	D3460	ao	MRSO	RMS	BLK	SS	
08389	D3504	ao	HNRS	HNR	EWS	CC	
08401	D3516	ao		HUN	HUN	HH	
08405	D3520	ao	MBDL	DBC	EWR	NL	
08423	D3538	ao		RMS	RMS	PD	
08428	D3543	ao	HNRL	HNR	EWS	BH (U)	
08441	D3556	ao	MBDL	RSS	RSS	BN	
08442	D3557	ao		ARV	LNW	EH (U)	
08445	D3560	ao		HUN	MAL	DD	
08447	D3562	ao		DST	DST	DS	
08460	D3575	ao	MBDL	RSS	RSS	LP	SPIRIT OF THE OAK
08484	D3599	ao	MBDL	RSS	RSS	WC	CAPTAIN NATHANIEL DARELL
08499	D3654	ao		PUL	BLE	CF	REDLIGHT
08500	D3655	ao	HNRL	HNR	EWS	BU (U)	
08502	D3657	ao	HNRL	HNR	NOR	BH	
08503	D3658	ao	HNRL	HNC	BLU	BIR	
08516	D3678	ao		ARV	LNW	BK	RORY
08527	D3689	ao	HNRL	HNR	TTG	PU	
08536	D3700	xo	HISE	LOR	BRW	DF (U)	
08567	D3734	ao	MBDL	AFS	EWS	ZG	
08568	D3735	xo	MBDL	KBR	RCG	ZH	St Rollox
08573	D3740	xo	MRSO	RMS	BLK	WO	
08578	D3745	ao	HNRS	HNR	EWS	LM (U)	
08580	D3747	xo	MBDL	RSS	EWS	BN	
08593	D3760	ao	MBDL	RSS	EWS	WI (U)	
08600	D3767, 97800	ao		AVD	AVD	MB	
08602	D3769	ao		BOM	BLE	ZD	

08613	D3780	ao		RMS	RMS	WO	
08615	D3782	ao	RFSH	WAB	BLK	LH	
08622	D3789	ao		RMS	BLK	KT	
08623	D3790	ao		HNR	DBS	HO (U)	
08629	D3796	xo	RCZN	KBR	KBR	ZN	*Wolverton*
08630	D3797	ao	HNRL	HNR	CEL	CC	*Celsa Endeavour*
08632	D3799	ao	MBDL	RSS	RSS	TR	
08643	D3810	xo	MBDL	AGI	GRE	MD	
08648	D3815	ao	MRSO	RMS	RMB	IS	
08649	D3816	xo	RCZN	KBR	KBR	ZN	*Bradwell*
08650	D3817	xow		AGI	BRY	ZG	*ISLE OF GRAIN*
08652	D3819	ao		AGI	BRY	MD	
08653	D3820	xo	HNRS	HNR	EWS	LM (U)	
08669	D3836	ao	RFSH	WAB	BLK	ZB	*Bob Machin*
08676	D3843	xo	HNRL	HNR	EWS	EKR	
08682	D3849	xo	KDSD	BOM	SPE	ZD	*Lionheart*
08685	D3852	ao	HNRS	HNR	EWS	EKR	
08700	D3867	xo		HNR	BRW	ZI	
08701	D3868	xo	HNRS	HNR	RES	LM (U)	
08703	D3870	ao	MBDL	RSS	EWS	SP	
08706	D3873	ao		HNR	EWS	WI (U)	
08709	D3876	xo	MBDL	RSS	EWS	WI (U)	
08711	D3878	ao	HNRS	HNR	RES	BU (U)	
08714	D3881	ao	MBDL	HNR	EWS	HO (U)	
08724	D3892	xo	HBSH	WAB	BLK	ZB	
08730	D3898	xo	RCZH	KBR	KBR	ZH	
08738	D3906	ao	MBDL	RSS	ECR	WI (U)	
08742	D3910	ao	HNRL	HNR	RES	DRC	
08743	D3911	ao	MBDL	ICI	BLE	BB	*Bryan Turner*
08750	D3918	xo	MRSO	RMS	BLK	WO (U)	
08752	D3920	ao	MBDL	RSS	EWS	WI (U)	
08754	D3922	ao	RMSX	RMS	RMS	NC	
08756	D3924	ao	MRSO	RMS	DEP	SS	
08762	D3930	ao	MRSO	RMS	BLK	DF	
08764	D3932	aod	ATZZ	RMS	BRW	PO	
08765	D3933	ao	HNRS	HNR	HNO	BH (U)	
08774	D3942	ao		AVD	AVD	MB	*ARTHUR VERNON DAWSON*
08782	D3950	ao	HNRL	HNR	COR	BH (U)	
08783	D3951	ao		EMR	EWS	ZO (U)	
08786	D3954	ao	HNRS	HNR	DEP	BH (U)	
08788	D3956	ao	MRSO	RMS	RMS	WO	
08798	D3966	ao		EMR	EWS	AT (U)	
08799	D3967	ao		HNR	EWS	EK	
08802	D3971	ao	HNRS	HNR	EWS	WI (U)	
08804	D3972	ao	WQDA	HNR	EWS	EK	
08809	D3977	xo	MRSO	RMS	RMS	PD	
08810	D3978	ao	MBDL	ARV	LNW	CP	*RICHARD J. WENHAM EASTLEIGH DEPOT*
08818	D3986	ao	HNRL	HNR	GBR	FG	*MOLLY*
08823	D3991	ao	KDSD	HUN	MAL	LH (U)	*LIBBIE*
08824	D3992	ao	HNRL	HNR	BLK	BH (U)	
08834	D4002	xo	HNRL	HNR	HNR	AN	
08846	D4014	xo		BOM	BLE	WI (U)	
08847	D4015	xow	MBDL	RMS	COT	NC	
08853	D4021	ao	RFSH	WAB	BLK	ZB	
08865	D4033	ao	HNRL	HNR	EWS	HO (U)	

08868	D4036	xo	MBDL	ARV	LNW	CP	
08870	D4038	xo	MBDL	RMS	CAS	KT	
08871	D4039	xo	MBDL	RMS	COT	ZI	
08872	D4040	xo		EMR	EWS	AT	
08873	D4041	ao	DDIN	HUN	RES	LH (U)	
08874	D4042	xo	MBDL	RMS	SIL	SS	
08877	D4045	xo	HNRS	HNR	DEP	BH	*WIGAN 1*
08879	D4047	xo	WQAA	AFS	EWS	ZG	
08885	D4115	xo		RMS	RMS	WO (U)	
08892	D4122	xo	HNRL	HNR	DRS	AH	
08903	D4133	ao	MBDL	ICI	BLE	BB	*John W Antill*
08904	D4134	ao	HNRL	HNR	EWS	CC	
08905	D4135	ao	HNRS	HNR	EWS	HO (U)	
08912	D4142	ao		AVD	BRW	MB (U)	
08913	D4143	ao		RMS	MAL	ZO (U)	
08918	D4148	xo	HNRS	HNR	DEP	BU (U)	
08921	D4151	ao		RSS	EWS	WI (U)	
08924	D4154	ao	HNRS	HNR	GBR	CC	
08927	D4157	xo	MBDL	AGO	GWS	RR	
08933	D4163	aow		AGI	BRY	MD	
08936	D4166	ao	MBDL	RMS	RMS	SS	
08939	D4169	ao	MBDL	RSS	ECR	WI (U)	
08943	D4173	xo	HNRL	HNR	HNR	CZ	
08944	D4174	xo		HNR	BLK	BQ (U)	
08947	D4177	ao		AGI	BRY	MD	
08954	D4184	ao	HNRL	HNR	BRW	PO	
08956	D4186	xo	CDJD	SEC	BRW	WI	
08994	D3577, 08462	ao	HNRS	HNR	EWS	BU (U)	

08738/939 are fitted with nose end scaffolding and AAR multiple working
08428/511/578/588/630/652/685/703/706/711/737/762/824/905/924/947 have swinghead couplers

Wabtec's 08724 rests in between shunting duties at the company's Doncaster repair facility on 28 March 2017. *Pip Dunn*

Class 09

09006	D3670	xo	HNRS	HNR	EWS	BU (U)	
09014	D4102	xo	HNRS	HNR	DEP	BU (U)	
09022	D4110	ao		VIC	BDB	BD	
09023	D4111	ao		EMR	EWS	AT (U)	
09106	D3927, 08759	ao	HNRL	HNR	HNR	DG	
09201	D3536, 08421	ao	HNRL	HNR	DEP	HO (U)	
09204	D3884, 08717	ao	MBDL	ARV	ARV	CP	

09023/106/201 have swinghead couplers

Class 20

20016	D8016	xo	HNRS	HNR	BRB	LM (U)	
20056	D8056	ao	HNRL	HNR	COY	SC (U)	
20066	D8066	ao		HNR	TAT	HO (U)	
20069	D8069	xo		HNR	BRB	MNR (U)	
20081	D8081	xop	HNRS	HNR	BRB	LM (U)	
20087	D8087	xop	MBDL	HNR	BRB	BQ (U)	
20088	D8088	xop	HNRS	HNR	RFS	LM (U)	
20110	D8110	xop		HNR	GYP	BQ (S)	
20121	D8121	aop	HNRS	HNR	HNO	BH (U)	
20166	D8166	aop	HNRL	HNR	HNO	DR (U)	
20168	D8168, 20304	aop	HNRL	HNR	HOP	HO	*SIR GEORGE EARLE*
20903	D8083, 20083	aotp	HNRS	HNR	DRU	BU (U)	
20904	D8041, 20041	aotp	HNRS	HNR	DRU	BU (U)	
20906	D8319, 20219	aotp	HNRL	HNR	HOP	HO	

Class 25

25057	D5207	xbp		HNR	BRB	NNR (U)	
25278	D7628	xo	MBDL	NYM	GYP	GO	*SYBILLA*
25313	D7663	xop		HNR	BRB	WEN (U)	
25283	D7633, 25904	xo		HNR	GYP	DFR (U)	

Class 31

31106	D5524	xo	RVLO	HJE	BRB	WO (U)	*Spalding Town*
31128	D5546	xop	NRLO	NEM	BRB	BU (S)	*Charybdis*
31285	D5817	ao	HNRL	HNR	NRY	WO	
31459	D5684, 31256	xe	RVLO	HNR	BRB	WO	
31461	D5547, 31129	xe	NRLO	NEM	CCE	BU (U)	
31465	D5637, 31213, 31565	aep	HNRL	HNR	NRY	WO	

Class 37

37198	D6898	xotp	MBDL	NET	NRY	DF (U)	
37255	D6955	xotp	NRLS	NEM	CCE	BU (U)	
37503	D6717, 37017	aotp	EPUK	EPX	EWS	LR (U)	
37510	D6812, 37112	aotp		EPX	DRC	LR (U)	

Class 47

47488	D1713	xet	NRLS	NEM	GYP	BU	
47701	D1932, 47493	xet	NRLO	NEM	TWO	BU (U)	*Waverley*
47703	D1960, 47514	xet	HNRS	HNR	UND	ZF (U)	

HNRC owns several Class 20s, some of which are hired to industrial customers. On 12 March 2016, D8110 (20110) stands at Scunthorpe Steelworks alongside one of the recently arrived Di8 locos. HNRC had three Class 20s based here at the time, but the contract has ended following the arrival of the ex-Norwegian locos. 20056 is still stored at the site but 20066 and 20110 have since left. *Pip Dunn*

The only Class 25 currently passed for the national network is D7628, but this is restricted to operations between Middlesbrough and Whitby only. On 27 June 2015 it stands at Grosmont with the rear of the 0919 to Whitby. *Pip Dunn*

Owned by HNRC but currently based at the Weardale Railway, ex-Network Rail 31465 works the 1045 Stanhope-Bishop Auckland past Holebeck on 21 April 2018. *Anthony Hicks*

47714	D1955, 47511	xet	HNRL	HNR	ANG	AH	
47715	D1945, 47502	xet	HNRL	HNR	NSD	WR	*Haymarket*
47744	D1927, 47250, 47600	xet	NRLS	NEM	EWS	BU (U)	
47769	D1753, 47491	xetm	HNRS	HNR	VIR	BH (U)	*Resolve*

Class 66

66048		aost		EMD	UND	ZW (U)	

Class 73

73133	E6040	xew	MBED	TMT	TMT	BM	

Class 86

86229	E3119	ae	EPEX	FLI	VIR	CB (U)	
86251	E3101	ae	EPEX	FLI	VIR	CB (U)	

Exported locomotives

Loco's current number	Previous UK numbers	Key detail difference	Current TOPS Sector	Vehicle Owner	Current Livery	Current depot allocation or location	Current name
Class 03							
D2156	03156	vo		ITY	BLU		
Class 08							
D3047	13047	vo		LAM	LAM		
D3092	13092	vo		LAM	LAM		
Note: Both these locos may have been scrapped							
Class 47							
92 70 00 47375-5	47375, D1894	aot	NRLO	CON	CSM	HUN	*FALCON*
Class 56							
92 55 0659 001-5	56101	ao		FLY	FLY	HUN	
92 55 0659 002-3	56115	ao		FLY	FLY	HUN	
92 55 0659 003-1	56117	ao		FLY	FER	HUN (U)	
Class 58							
	58001	aosp	WQCA	DBC	ETF	AZ (U)	
	58004	aosp	WQCA	DBC	TSO	AZ (U)	
	58005	aosp	WQCA	DBC	ETF	AZ (U)	
	58006	aosp	WQCA	DBC	ETF	AZ (U)	
	58007	aosp	WQCA	DBC	TSO	AZ (U)	
	58009	aosp	WQCA	DBC	TSO	AZ (U)	
	58010	aosp	WQCA	DBC	TSO	AZ (U)	
	58011	aosp	WQCA	DBC	TSO	AZ (U)	
	58013	aosp	WQCA	DBC	ETF	AZ (U)	
L54	58015	aosp		TFA	CON	AC	
	58018	aosp	WQCA	DBC	TSO	AZ (U)	
L43	58020	aosp		TFA	CON	AC	
	58021	aosp	WQCA	DBC	ETF	AZ (U)	
L42	58024	aosp		TFA	CON	AC	
	58025	aosp	WQCA	DBC	CON	AB (U)	
	58026	aosp	WQCA	DBC	TSO	AZ (U)	
L52	58027	aosp	WQCA	DBC	CON	AB (U)	
L44	58029	aosp		TFA	CON	AC (U)	
L46	58030	aosp		TFA	CON	AC	
L45	58031	aosp		TFA	CON	AC	*Caballero Ferroviario*
	58032	aosp	WQCA	DBC	ETF	AZ (U)	
	58033	aosp	WQCA	DBC	TSO	AZ (U)	
	58034	aosp	WQCA	DBC	TSO	AZ (U)	
	58035	aosp	WQCA	DBC	TSO	AZ (U)	
	58036	aosp	WQCA	DBC	ETF	AZ (U)	

While on hire to Dutch operator ACTS, 5811 (ex-58039) stands at Amersfoort Pon on a charter from Rotterdam to Arnhem on 21 June 2008. This loco and its two ACTS compatriots later moved for work in France but are currently withdrawn in that country pending disposal or reuse. *Pip Dunn*

5814	58038	aosp	WCQA	TFA	ETF	AZ (U)
5811	58039	aosp	WQCA	DBC	ETF	AZ (U)
	58040	aosp	WQCA	DBC	TSO	AZ (U)
L36	58041	aosp		TFA	CON	AB (U)
	58042	aosp	WQCA	DBC	ETF	AZ (U)
L37	58043	aosp		TFA	CON	AC
5812	58044	aosp	WQCA	DBC	ETF	WP (U)
	58046	aosp	WQCA	DBC	TSO	AZ (U)
L51	58047	aosp		TFA	CON	AC
	58049	aosp	WQCA	DBC	ETF	AZ (U)
L53	58050	aosp	WQCA	DBC	CON	AB (U)

Class 66

92 70 0 066010-4	66010	aos	WGEA	DBC	EWS	AZ
92 70 0 066022-9	66022	aos	WGEA	DBC	EWS	AZ
92 70 0 066026-0	66026	aos	WGEA	DBC	EWS	AZ
92 70 0 066028-6	66028	aos	WGEA	DBC	EWS	AZ
92 70 0 066029-4	66029	aos	WGEA	DBC	EWS	AZ
92 70 0 066032-8	66032	aos	WGEA	DBC	EWS	AZ
92 70 0 066033-6	66033	aos	WGEA	DBC	EWS	AZ
92 70 0 066036-9	66036	aos	WGEA	DBC	EWS	AZ
92 70 0 066038-5	66038	aos	WGEA	DBC	EWS	AZ
92 70 0 066042-7	66042	aos	WGEA	DBC	EWS	AZ
92 70 0 066045-0	66045	aos	WGEA	DBC	EWS	AZ
92 70 0 066049-2	66049	aos	WGEA	DBC	EWS	AZ
92 70 0 066052-6	66052	aos	WGEA	DBC	EWS	AZ
92 70 0 066062-5	66062	aos	WGEA	DBC	EWS	AZ
92 70 0 066064-1	66064	aos	WGEA	DBC	EWS	AZ
92 70 0 066071-6	66071	aos	WGEA	DBC	EWS	AZ

92 70 0 066072-4	66072	aos	WGEA	DBC	EWS	AZ
92 70 0 066073-2	66073	aos	WGEA	DBC	EWS	AZ
92 70 0 066123-5	66123	aos	WGEA	DBC	EWS	AZ
92 70 0 066146-6	66146	aos	WGEP	DBC	EWS	PN
92 70 0 066153-2	66153	aos	WGEP	DBC	EWS	PN
92 70 0 066157-3	66157	aos	WGEP	DBC	EWS	PN
92 70 0 066159-9	66159	aos	WGEP	DBC	EWS	PN
92 70 0 066163-1	66163	aos	WGEP	DBC	DBR	PN
92 70 0 066166-4	66166	aos	WGEP	DBC	EWS	PN
92 70 0 066173-0	66173	aos	WGEP	DBC	EWS	PN
92 70 0 066178-9	66178	aos	WGEP	DBC	DBR	PN
92 70 0 066179-7	66179	aos	WGEA	DBC	EWS	AZ
92 70 0 066180-5	66180	aos	WGEP	DBC	EWS	PN
92 70 0 066189-6	66189	aos	WGEP	DBC	DBR	PN
92 70 0 066190-4	66190	aos	WGEA	DBC	EWS	AZ
92 70 0 066191-2	66191	aos	WGEA	DBC	EWS	AZ
92 70 0 066193-8	66193	aos	WGEA	DBC	EWS	AZ
92 70 0 066195-3	66195	aos	WGEA	DBC	EWS	AZ
92 70 0 066196-1	66196	aos	WGEP	DBC	EWS	PN
92 70 0 066201-9	66201	aos	WGEA	DBC	EWS	AZ
92 70 0 066202-7	66202	aos	WGEA	DBC	EWS	AZ
92 70 0 066203-5	66203	aos	WGEA	DBC	EWS	AZ
92 70 0 066204-3	66204	aos	WGEA	DBC	EWS	AZ
92 70 0 066205-1	66205	aos	WGEA	DBC	EWS	AZ
92 70 0 066208-4	66208	aos	WGEA	DBC	EWS	AZ
92 70 0 066209-2	66209	aos	WGEA	DBC	EWS	AZ
92 70 0 066210-0	66210	aos	WGEA	DBC	EWS	AZ
92 70 0 066211-8	66211	aos	WGEA	DBC	EWS	AZ
92 70 0 066212-6	66212	aos	WGEA	DBC	EWS	AZ
92 70 0 066213-4	66213	aos	WGEA	DBC	EWS	AZ
92 70 0 066214-2	66214	aos	WGEA	DBC	EWS	AZ
92 70 0 066215-9	66215	aos	WGEA	DBC	EWS	AZ
92 70 0 066216-7	66216	aos	WGEA	DBC	EWS	AZ
92 70 0 066217-5	66217	aos	WGEA	DBC	EWS	AZ
92 70 0 066218-3	66218	aos	WGEA	DBC	EWS	AZ
92 70 0 066219-1	66219	aos	WGEA	DBC	EWS	AZ
92 70 0 066220-9	66220	aos	WGEP	DBC	DBR	PN
92 70 0 066222-5	66222	aos	WGEA	DBC	EWS	AZ
92 70 0 066223-3	66223	aos	WGEA	DBC	EWS	AZ
92 70 0 066224-1	66224	aos	WGEA	DBC	EWS	AZ
92 70 0 066225-8	66225	aos	WGEA	DBC	EWS	AZ
92 70 0 066226-6	66226	aos	WGEA	DBC	EWS	AZ
92 70 0 066227-4	66227	aos	WGEP	DBC	DBR	PN
92 70 0 066228-2	66228	aos	WGEA	DBC	EWS	AZ
92 70 0 066229-0	66229	aos	WGEA	DBC	EWS	AZ
92 70 0 066231-6	66231	aos	WGEA	DBC	EWS	AZ
92 70 0 066232-4	66232	aos	WGEA	DBC	EWS	AZ
92 70 0 066233-2	66233	aos	WGEA	DBC	EWS	AZ
92 70 0 066234-0	66234	aos	WGEA	DBC	EWS	AZ
92 70 0 066235-7	66235	aos	WGEA	DBC	EWS	AZ
92 70 0 066236-5	66236	aos	WGEA	DBC	EWS	AZ
92 70 0 066237-3	66237	aos	WGEP	DBC	EWS	PN
92 70 0 066239-9	66239	aos	WGEA	DBC	EWS	AZ
92 70 0 066240-7	66240	aos	WGEA	DBC	EWS	AZ
92 70 0 066241-5	66241	aos	WGEA	DBC	EWS	AZ
92 70 0 066242-3	66242	aos	WGEA	DBC	EWS	AZ

92 70 0 066243-1	66243	aos	WGEA	DBC	EWS	AZ
92 70 0 066244-9	66244	aos	WGEA	DBC	EWS	AZ
92 70 0 066245-6	66245	aos	WGEA	DBC	EWS	AZ
92 70 0 066246-4	66246	aos	WGEA	DBC	EWS	AZ
92 70 0 066247-2	66247	aos	WGEA	DBC	EWS	AZ
92 70 0 066248-9	66248	aos	WGEP	DBC	DBR	PN
92 70 0 066249-8	66249	aos	WGEA	DBC	EWS	AZ
66013	66411	aos	DHLT	MAQ	FPH	FP
66015	66412	aos	DHLT	MAQ	FPH	FP
66014	66417	aos	DHLT	MAQ	FPH	FP
66016	66527	aos	DHLT	EVS	FLR	FP
66017	66530	aos	DHLT	POR	FLR	FP
66018	66535	aos	DHLT	POR	FLR	FP
66009	66582	aos	DHLT	EVS	FLR	FP
66010	66583	aos	DHLT	EVS	FLR	FP
66011	66584	aos	DHLT	EVS	FLR	FP
66008	66586	aos	DHLT	MAQ	FLR	FP
	66595	aos	DHLT	BEA	FLR	FP
66603	66608	aos	DHLT	POR	FLR	FP
66605	66609	aos	DHLT	POR	FLR	FP
66604	66611	aos	DHLT	POR	FLR	FP
66606	66612	aos	DHLT	POR	FLR	FP
66602	66624	aos	DHLT	MAQ	FLR	FP
66601	66625	aos	DHLT	MAQ	FLR	FP
	66954	aos	DHLT	BEA	FLR	FP

Note: The Freightliner Poland locos have been renumbered in the 660xx series for Class 66/5s and 6660x series for Class 66/6s. FPL also owns seven 'Class 66s' numbered 66001-007, which were new-build locos and did not work in the UK

DB Cargo's Euro Cargo Rail subsidiary also operates 60 'Class 66s', numbered 77001-060, which were new-build locos and did not work in the UK

All WGEP locos have their swinghead couplers removed. WGEA locos retain them

Class 86

91 52 00 85003-2	86213, E3193	ae	BMT	BMT	BUL	*Lancashire Witch*
91 55 0450 005-6	86215, E3165	ae	FLY	FLY	HUN	
91 55 0450 006-6	86217, 86504, E3177	ae	FLY	FLY	HUN	
91 55 0450 004-1	86218, E3175	ae	FLY	FLY	HUN	
91 55 0450 007-4	86228, E3167	ae	FLY	FLY	HUN	
9152 00 85005-2	86231, E3126	ae	BMT	BMT	BUL	*Lady of the Lake*
91 55 0450 003-3	86232, E3113	ae	FLY	FLY	HUN	
	86233, 86506, E3172	ae	BMT	EBY	BUL (U)	
9152 00 85006-2	86234, E3155	ae	BMT	BMT	BUL	
9152 00 85004-7	86235, E3194	ae	BMT	BMT	BUL	*Novelty*
91 55 0450 008-2	86242, E3138	ae	FLY	FLY	HUN	
91 55 0450 001-7	86248, E3107	ae	FLY	FLY	HUN	
91 55 0450 002-5	86250, E3189	ae	FLY	FLY	HUN	
91 55 0450 009-0	86424, E3111, 86024, 86324	ae	FLY	NRY	HUN (U)	
91 52 00 85001-6	86701, E3128, 86205, 86503	ae	BMT	BMT	BUL	*Orion*
91 52 00 85002-4	86702 E3144, 86048, 86260	ae	BMT	BMT	BUL	*Cassiopeia*

Class 87

91 52 00 87003-7	87003	ae	BZK	BZK	BUL	
91 52 00 87004-5	87004	ae	BZK	BRZ	BUL	*Britannia*
91 52 00 87006-0	87006	ae	BZK	DGB	BUL (U)	
91 52 00 87007-8	87007	ae	BZK	COT	BUL	
91 52 00 87008-9	87008	ae	BZK	COT	BUL (U)	
91 52 00 87009-4	87009	ae	BMT	BMT	BUL	
91 52 00 87010-2	87010	ae	BZK	BZK	BUL	
91 52 00 87012-8	87012	ae	BZK	NSE	BUL	
91 52 00 87013-6	87013	ae	BZK	BZK	BUL	
91 52 00 87014-7	87014	ae	BZK	BZK	BUL (U)	
91 52 00 87017-7	87017	ae	BMT	EPX	BUL	*Iron Duke*
91 52 00 87019-3	87019	ae	BZK	LNR	BUL	
91 52 00 87020-1	87020	ae	BZK	BZK	BUL	
91 52 00 87022-7	87022	ae	BZK	DGB	BUL	
91 52 00 87023-5	87023	ae	BMT	EPX	BUL	*Velocity*
91 52 00 87025-0	87025	ae	BMT	BMT	BUL	
91 52 00 87026-8	87026	ae	BZK	BZK	BUL	
91 52 00 87028-4	87028	ae	BZK	DRS	BUL	
91 52 00 87029-2	87029	ae	BZK	BZK	BUL	
91 52 00 87033-4	87033	ae	BZK	BZK	BUL	
91 52 00 87034-2	87034	ae	BZK	BZK	BUL (U)	

Class 92

91 53 0 472 002-1	92001	ae	WGEE	TRA	DBR	CRO	
91 53 0 472 003-9	92002	ae	WGEE	TRA	DBZ	CRO	
	92003	ae	WGEE	TRA	EUE	CRO (U)	*Beethoven*
91 53 0 472 005-4	92005	ae	WGEE	TRA	TRA	CRO	
91 53 0 472 001-3	92012	ae	WGEE	TRA	DBR	CRO	
88002	92022	ae	WGEE	DBC	EUE	DM (U)	*Charles Dickens*
91 53 0 472 004-7	92024	ae	WGEE	TRA	TRB	CRO	
91 70 00 92025-1	92025	ae	WGEE	DBC	EUE	DK	*Oscar Wilde*
	92026	ae	WGEE	TRA	EUE	CRO (U)	*Britten*
91 70 00 92027-7	92027	ae	WGEE	DBC	EUE	DK	*George Eliot*
91 52 16 88030-1	92030	ae	WGEE	DBC	EUE	DK	*Ashford*
91 70 00 92034-3	92034	ae	WGEE	DBC	EUE	DK	*Kipling*
91 53 0 472 006-2	92039	ae	WGEE	TRA	DBR	CRO	

3 Preserved locomotives

This section list all the locos classed as preserved, including those that are owned by preservation groups for the supply of spare parts and unlikely to ever be restored.

Those locos owned by preservation groups but are main line registered and either on long-term hire to FOCs/TOCs or used for charter work or spot hire are included in section 1.

Names are listed even if the plates are not presently fitted because the loco is part way through overhaul.

Locos are listed at their home railway unless on a long-term loam, but locos do move about and visit other railways or sites.

Loco	previous numbers	key detail differences	livery	location	status	name
Class 01						
D2953	11503	o	GWS	PKR	OP	
D2956	11506	o	BLK	ELR	OP	

Note: Locos do not have train brakes

One of two preserved Class 01 shunters, D2953 operates brake van rides at Rowsley, Peak Rail, on 26 September 2009. *Pip Dunn*

Class 02

02003	D2853	vo	GWS	BH	OP	
	D2854	vo	GWS	PKR	OP	
	D2858	vo	GWS	MRB	UR	
	D2860	vo	GWS	NRM	OP	
	D2866	vo	BRW	PKR	UR	
	D2867	vo	IND	BAT	OP	
	D2868	vo	GWS	PKR	OP	

Class 03

03018	D2018	vo	BRW	MRM	UR	
03020	D2020	vo	BRW	MRM	SU	
03022	D2022	vo	BRB	SCR	UR	
	D2023	vo	GWS	KES	OP	
	D2024	vo	IND	KES	SU	
03027	D2027	vo	BRW	PKR	UR	
03037	D2037	vo	BLK	RDR	SU	
	D2041	vo	BLK	CVR	OP	
	D2046	vo	IND	PVR	UR	
	D2051	vo	GNY	NNR	SU	
03059	D2059	xow	GWS	IWR	OP	
03062	D2062	xow	GWS	ELR	OP	
03063	D2063	xow	BRW	NNR	UR	
03066	D2066	xow	BRW	BH	OP	
03069	D2069	vo	GWS	VBR	UR	
03072	D2072	vo	GWS	LHR	OP	
03073	D2073	xow	BRW	RAC	OP	
03078	D2078	xow	BLK	NTR	OP	
03079	D2079	vo	BRW	DVR	OP	
03081	D2081	vo	BRW	MRM	OP	
03089	D2089	xow	GWS	MRM	OP	
03090	D2090	vo	GNY	NRS	OP	
03094	D2094	xow	GWS	RDR	OP	
03099	D2099	vo	BRW	PKR	OP	
03112	D2112	xow	GWS	RVR	OP	
03113	D2113	vo	BRW	PKR	OP	
	D2117	vo	MAR	LHR	OP	
03118	D2118	vo	BRW	GCN	UR	
03119	D2119	vo	IND	EOR	OP	
03120	D2120	vo	GNY	FHR	OP	
	D2133	vo	GWS	WSR	OP	
03134	D2134	vo	IND	RDR	OP	
	D2138	vo	GWS	MRB	OP	
	D2139	vo	GNY	PKR	OP	
03141	D2141	vo	IND	PBR	UR	
03144	D2144	vo	BRW	WR	OP	
03145	D2145	vo	BRW	MOL	OP	
	D2148	vo	GWS	RSR	UR	
03152	D2152	vo	GRE	SCR	OP	
03158	D2158	xow	GWS	TIT	OP	*MARGARET-ANN*
03162	D2162	xow	BRW	LLR	UR	
03170	D2170	xow	BRW	EOR	OP	
	D2178	vo	GWS	GIR	OP	
03179	D2179	xo	UND	RHR	UR	

Class 03 diesel mechanical shunter D2133 in between station pilot duties at Minehead on 9 June 2018. *Pip Dunn*

03180	D2180	xow	BRW	PKR	SU	
	D2182	vo	GRN	GWR	OP	
	D2184	vo	BLK	CVR	OP	
03189	D2189	vo	BRW	RSR	OP	
	D2192	vo	BLK	PDR	OP	*TITAN*
03197	D2197	xow	BRW	MRM	UR	
	D2199	xow	GWS	PKR	OP	
03371	D2371	xow	BRW	PDR	OP	
03399	D2399	xow	BRW	MRM	OP	
03901	D2128, 03128	xo	BLK	PKR	OP	

Note: 03079/119/120/141/144/145/152/179 have reduced height cabs

Class 04

	D2203	vo	GNY	EBR	OP
	D2205	vo	GSW	PKR	OP
	D2207	vo	GWS	NYM	UR
	D2229	vo	GRE	PR	SU
	D2245	vo	GWS	DVR	OP
	D2246	vo	GWS	SDR	OP
	D2271	vo	IND	WSR	SU
	D2272	vo	GRE	PKR	UR
	D2279	vo	BLK	PKR	OP
	D2280	vo	BLK	NNR	SU
	D2284	vo	GWS	PR	OP
	D2289	ao	IND	PR	UR
	D2298	vo	GNY	BRC	OP
	D2302	vo	GWS	MOL	OP
04110	D2310	vo	BLU	BAT	OP
	D2324	vo	IND	BU	SU

Immaculate in British Railways green, Class 04 Drewry shunter D2284 rests at Rowsley, Peak Rail, on 26 September 2009. *Pip Dunn*

	D2325	vo	GWS	MRM	OP	
	D2334	vo	GWS	MNR	OP	
	D2337	vo	GWS	PKR	OP	

Class 05

05001	D2554, 97803	vo	GWS	IWR	OP
	D2578	vo	GWS	MOL	OP
	D2587	vo	GWS	PKR	OP
	D2595	vo	GWS	RSR	OP

Class 06

06003	D2420, 97804	vo	GWS	PR	UR

Class 07

07001	D2985	xow	BRW	PKR	OP
07005	D2989	xow	IND	GCR	SU
07010	D2994	vo	BRW	AVR	OP
07012	D2996	vo	BRW	BH	OP
07013	D2997	xow	BRW	ELR	SU

Class 08

	D3000	vo	GNY	PKR	UR	
	D3002	vo	BLK	PVR	OP	
	D3014	vo	BRW	PDR	OP	*SAMSON*

08011	D3018	vo	GWS	CPR	OP	*HAVERSHAM*
	D3019	vo	UND	CRT	UR	
08015	D3022	vo	GWS	SVR	OP	
08016	D3023	vo	BRW	PKR	OP	
08022	D3030	vo	IND	CWR	OP	*LION*
08032	D3044	vo	BRW	MHR	OP	*MENDIP*
08046	D3059	vo	BRW	CAL	OP	*BRECHIN CITY*
08054	D3067	vo	BRB	EBR	UR	
08060	D3074	vo	IND	CWR	OP	*UNICORN*
08064	D3079	vo	BLK	NRS	UR	
	D3101	vo	BLK	GCR	OP	
08102	D3167	vo	GWS	LWR	OP	
08108	D3174	vo	BLK	KES	SU	*Dover Castle*
08114	D3180	vo	GRE	GCN	OP	
08123	D3190	vo	GRE	CWR	OP	
08133	D3201	vo	GWS	SVR	OP	
08164	D3232	vo	BRW	ELR	OP	*PRUDENCE*
	D3255	vo	UND	MAL	UR	
	D3261	vo	BLK	SCR	OP	
08195	D3265	vo	BLK	LLR	OP	
08202	D3272	ao	EEG	AVR	OP	
08238	D3308	vo	BRW	DFR	OP	*Charlie*
08266	D3336	vo	DEP	KWV	OP	
08288	D3358	vo	BLK	MHR	OP	
08331	D3401	ao	BLK	MRB	OP	
08359	D3429	vo	GWS	TSR	OP	
08377	D3462	vo	GWS	WSR	OP	
08436	D3551	xo	LSW	SWR	OP	
08443	D3558	vo	GWS	BKR	OP	
08444	D3559	vo	GWS	BWR	OP	
08471	D3586	vo	GWS	SVR	OP	
08473	D3588	vo	BRW	DFR	SU	
08476	D3591	vo	BLK	SWR	OP	
08479	D3594	vo	BRW	ELR	OP	
08490	D3605	vo	BLK	STR	OP	
08495	D3610	xo	BRW	NYM	UR	
08528	D3690	xo	GWS	GCR	OP	
08556	D3723	vo	GWS	NYM	OP	
08590	D3757	xo	BRW	MRB	OP	
08598	D3765	ao	POT	CHR	OP	
08604	D3771	xo	BRW	DRC	OP	*PHANTOM*
08605	D3772	ao	DBS	EVR	OP	
08633	D3800	ao	EWS	CHV	UR	
08635	D3802	xo	BRW	SVR	UR	
08694	D3861	xo	EWS	GCR	UR	
08757	D3925	ao	RES	TBR	UR	
08767	D3935	xo	GWS	NNR	SU	
08769	D3937	vo	GWS	SVR	OP	*Gladys*
08772	D3940	xo	GWS	NNR	OP	
08773	D3941	xo	BRW	EBR	OP	
08784	D3952	ao	EWS	GCN	OP	
08825	D3993	xo	BRW	CPR	OP	
08830	D3998	xow	BLK	PKR	OP	
08850	D4018	xow	BRB	NYM	OP	
08881	D4095	ao	GWS	SDR	OP	
08888	D4118	ao	EWS	KES	OP	

Class 08 D3586 is stationed at Bridgnorth shed on the Severn Valley Railway and is seen in between duties on 3 October 2015. *Pip Dunn*

08896	D4126	xo	EWS	SVR	SU	
08907	D4137	ao	DBS	GCR	OP	
08911	D4141	xo	NRM	NRM	OP	*MATEY*
08915	D4145	xo	BRW	NTR	OP	
08922	D4152	ao	EWS	GCN	OP	
08937	D4167	xo	GWS	DAR	OP	*BLUEBELL MEL*
08993	D3759, 08592	xo	EWS	KWV	OP	*ASHBURNHAM*
08995	D3854, 08687	ao	EWS	WIS	UR	

Note: 08993-995 have reduced body height
08633 has a swinghead coupler

Class 09

09001	D3665	xow	EWS	PKR	OP	
09004	D3668	xow	BRW	SCR	OP	
09010	D3721	xow	GWS	SDR	OP	
09012	D4100	xow	GWS	SVR	OP	*Dick Hardy*
09015	D4103	xo	DEP	WIS	SU	
09017	D4105	xo	NRM	NRM	OP	
09018	D4106	xow	GWS	BLU	OP	
09019	D4107	xow	GWS	WSR	OP	
09024	D4112	xo	DEP	ELR	OP	
09025	D4113	xo	GWS	EKR	OP	
09026	D4114	xow	GWS	SPA	OP	*Cedric Wares*
09107	D4013, 08845	aow	BRW	SVR	UR	

While several Class 10s were repainted into British Rail blue, none were renumbered. However, D4067 at the Great Central Railway now carries 10119, which would have most likely been its TOPS number had it lasted into the mid-1970s. On 3 March 2013, it was stabled at Loughborough. *Pip Dunn*

Class 10

	D3452	vo	BLK	BWR	OP	
	D3489	xo	BLK	SPA	OP	*COLONEL TOMLINE*
10119	D4067	vo	BRW	GCR	OP	*Margaret Ethel - Thomas Alfred Naylor*
	D4092	vo	GWS	BH	UR	

Class 11

12052	vo	IND	CAL	SU	
12077	vo	GWS	MRB	OP	
12082	xo	GWS	MHR	OP	
12083	vo	BLE	BAT	SU	
12088	vo	GWS	ALN	OP	
12093	vo	GWS	CAL	OP	
12099	vo	BLK	SVR	OP	
12131	vo	BLK	NNR	OP	

Class 12

15224	vo	GWS	SPA	OP	

Unclassified locos

	D2511	vo	GWS	KWV	OP	
	D2767	vo	GWS	BKR	OP	
	D2774	vo	GWS	STR	OP	
	18000	vo	GWR	DRC	SU	

Class 14

	D9500	vo	GWS	PKR	UR	
	D9502	vo	GWS	ELR	UR	
	D9504	xo	GWS	KES	OP	
	D9513	vo	NCB	FBR	OP	
	D9516	xo	GWS	DRC	OP	
	D9518	vo	NCB	WSR	UR	
	D9520	xo	GWS	NVR	OP	
	D9521	vo	GWS	DFR	OP	
	D9523	xo	MWS	WEN	OP	
14901	D9524	xo	BLU	CVR	OP	
	D9525	vo	GWS	PKR	OP	
	D9526	vo	GWS	WSR	OP	
14029	D9529	xo	BRB	NVR	OP	
	D9531	xo	GWS	ELR	OP	*ERNEST*
	D9537	vo	BLK	ELR	OP	
	D9539	vo	GWS	RSR	OP	
	D9551	vo	GOP	SVR	OP	
	D9553	vo	GWS	VBR	UR	
	D9555	vo	GWS	DFR	OP	

Class 14 D9551 is painted in Golden Ochre livery, never before seen on the type prior to completion of its restoration in 2016. On 19 May 2018, it waits to leave with the 1237 Kidderminster-Bewdley. *Pip Dunn*

Sole surviving Class 17 Clayton D8568 approaches Thame Junction on 9 April 2017 with the 1100 from Chinnor. *Martin Loader*

Class 15

DB968000	D8233	vo	GYP	ELR	UR

Note: loco has a through steam pipe

Class 17

	D8568	vo	GFY	CPR	OP

Note: loco has a through steam pipe

Class 20

20001	D8001	xo	GFY	MRB	OP
20020	D8020	xo	BRB	BKR	UR
20031	D8031	xop	TLC	KWV	OP
20048	D8048	xo	BRB	MRB	UR
20050	D8000	vo	GNY	NRM	UR
20057	D8057	xo	GYP	CRV	UR
20059	D8059	xo	GYP	CPR	OP
20063	D8063	xo	CFD	BAT	UR
20098	D8098	xop	GNY	GCR	OP
20137	D8137	xop	GFY	GWR	OP
20154	D8154	xop	BRB	GCN	OP
20169	D8169	xop	UND	WEN	UR
20188	D8188	xop	GYP	MRB	OP
20214	D8314	xop	GYP	LHR	OP
20228	D8128	xop	BRB	BIR	UR

Note: 20050 has a through steam pipe
Note: 20228 was numbered CFD2004 while owned by CFD in France

Main line registered, but preserved by the Class 20 Locomotive Society, 20227 stands at Sheringham on 11 May 2018 having arrived with the 1035 from Holt. This loco has since been named *Sherlock Holmes*. *Pip Dunn*

Class 23

	D5910	xo	UND	BH	UC

Note: This is a new build loco still under construction. It uses parts of the bodyshell of 37372 (D6859, 37159), which is now regarded as disposed of

Class 24

24032	D5032	vi	GYP	NYM	UR	
24054	D5054, TDB968008	vb	GYP	ELR	UR	*PHIL SOUTHERN*
24061	D5061, RDB968007, 97201	vb	GNY	NYM	UR	
24081	D5081	vo	BRB	GWR	UR	

Class 25

25035	D5185	xip	GYP	GCR	OP	
25059	D5209	xbp	BRB	KWV	OP	
25067	D5217	vb	GYP	BU	SU	
25072	D5222	xi	GRE	CAL	SU	
25083	D5233	vip	BRB	CAL	SU	
25173	D7523	xo	GYP	BAT	UR	
25185	D7535	xo	BYP	PDR	OP	*MERCURY*
25191	D7541	xop	GYP	SDR	UR	
25235	D7585	xip	BRB	BKR	UR	
25244	D7594	xop	UND	KES	SU	
25262	D7612, 25901	xo	GYP	SDR	OP	

25265	D7615	xo	BRB	BU	SU	
25279	D7629	xo	GYP	ELR	OP	
25309	D7659, 25909	xo	UND	PKR	UR	
25321	D7671	xop	GYP	MRB	UR	
25322	D7672, 25912	xop	BRU	CHV	UR	*TAMWORTH CASTLE*

Class 26

26001	D5301	xo	GNY	LHR	OP	
26002	D5302	xo	GNY	STR	SU	
26004	D5304	xo	TLC	BU	SU	
26007	D5300	xo	RSR	BH	OP	
26010	D5310	xo	GFY	LLR	OP	
26011	D5311	xo	BRB	BU	SU	
26014	D5314	xo	GNY	CAL	OP	
26024	D5324	xop	BRB	BKR	UR	
26025	D5325	xop	GNY	STR	SU	
26035	D5335	xop	BRB	CAL	SU	
26038	D5338	xop	BRB	NYM	OP	*Tom Clift 1954-2012*
26040	D5340	xop	BRB	WAV	UR	
26043	D5343	xop	BRB	GWR	OP	

Class 27

27001	D5347	xip	BRB	BKR	OP
27005	D5351	xbp	BRB	BKR	UR
27007	D5353	vop	UND	CAL	SU
27024	D5370, ADB968028	xop	GYP	CAL	OP
27050	D5394, 27106	xip	GNY	STR	OP
27056	D5401, 27112	xip	GFY	GCR	UR
27059	D5410, 27123, 27205	xotp	UND	LR	UR
27066	D5386, 27103, 27212	xotp	BRB	BH	UR

One of 20 preserved Class 25s, 25059 stands at Haworth on 21 May 2013 with a period goods train.
Anthony Hicks

The first-built Class 26, which dates from 1958, 26007 calls at Finghall on the Wensleydale Railway with a Leeming Bar-Redmire train on 16 July 2016. This loco has recently been repainted into Original Railfreight livery, first seen on the class in 1985. *Pip Dunn*

One of eight surviving Class 27s, D5401 is currently stopped for overhaul but on 26 October 2010 it was visiting the Kent & East Sussex Railway and has just arrived at Bodiam with the 1245 from Tenterden. *Pip Dunn*

Class 28

D5705	ADB968006, S15705	vo	GYP	ELR	UR

Class 31

31018	D5500	vi	BRB	NRM	SU	
31101	D5518	xb	BRB	AVR	OP	
31108	D5526	xop	RFO	MRB	OP	
31119	D5537	xo	BRB	EBR	SU	
31130	D5548	xop	RFO	AVR	UR	
31162	D5580	xi	BRB	MRB	OP	
31203	D5627	xo	GNY	PBR	OP	Steve Ogden GM
31206	D5630	xo	CCE	RHR	OP	
31207	D5631	xo	GNY	NNR	UR	
31210	D5634	xop	RFO	DFR	UR	
31235	D5662	xo	BRB	DFR	UR	
31255	D5683	xo	EWS	MNR	UR	
31270	D5800	xop	REG	PKR	SU	Athena
31271	D5801	xop	TLA	NVR	OP	Stratford 1840-2001
31289	D5821	xo	EBP	RHR	OP	PHŒNIX
31327	D5862	xo	GYP	STR	OP	
31414	D5814	xe	GYP	MRB	UR	
31418	D5522	xei	BRB	MRB	UR	
31430	D5695, 31265, 31530	xy	BRB	MRM	OP	Sister Dora
31435	D5600, 31179	xe	GYE	EBR	SU	
31438	D5557, 31139, 31538	xe	BRB	EOR	OP	
31466	D5533, 31115	xe	EWS	DFR	OP	
31563	D5830, 31297, 31463	xy	GOP	GCR	OP	
31601	D5609, 31186	xozf	DCR	EVR	OP	Devon Diesel Society
97205	D5581, 31163	xo	RTC	CPR	OP	

A star of the preserved scene is the A1A Locomotive Ltd's 31271 *Stratford Depot 1840-2001*. It poses in the sunshine at Wansford with BR blue 31459 on 13 October 2017. *Pip Dunn*

The Class 33/1 Preservation Group's 33108 is on long-term secondment to the Severn Valley Railway and was at Kidderminster on 19 May 2018. *Pip Dunn*

Class 33

33002	D6501	xyp	GYP	SDR	OP	
33008	D6508	xyp	GYP	BAT	UR	*Eastleigh*
33018	D6530	xyp	BRB	MRM	UR	
33019	D6534	xyp	DUT	BAT	UR	*Griffon*
33021	D6539	xyp	BRB	CHV	UR	*Captain Charles*
33035	D6553	xyp	BRB	WR	OP	
33046	D6564	xyp	SWT	ELR	SU	
33048	D6566	xyp	GYP	WSR	OP	
33052	D6570	xyp	GNY	KES	SU	*Ashford*
33053	D6571	xyp	BRB	LR	UR	
33057	D6575	xep	GYP	WSR	OP	
33063	D6583	xep	TMF	SPA	OP	*RJ Mitchell – DESIGNER OF THE SPITFIRE*
33065	D6585	xep	BRB	SPA	UR	*Sealion*
33102	D6513	xew	BRB	CHV	OP	*Sophie*
33103	D6514	xewp	DEP	EVR	OP	*SWORDFISH*
33108	D6521	xew	BRB	SVR	OP	
33109	D6525	xew	DEP	ELR	OP	*Captain Bill Smith RNR*
33110	D6527	xew	DEP	BWR	OP	
33111	D6528	xew	BRB	SWR	OP	
33116	D6535	xewp	BRB	GCR	OP	
33117	D6536	xew	BRB	ELR	UR	
33201	D6586	xesp	BRB	SWR	OP	
33202	D6587	xesp	BRB	MHR	OP	*Dennis G. Robinson*
33208	D6593	xesp	GYP	BAT	SU	

Preserved D6566, formerly 33048, leads the 1648 Bishops Lydeard-Minehead on the approach to Williton on 10 June 2018. *Anthony Hicks*

Class 35

D7017	vop	GYP	WSR	OP
D7018	vop	GYP	WSR	UR
D7029	vop	BRB	SVR	UR
D7076	vbp	BRB	ELR	OP

Class 35 Hymek D7017 is based at the West Somerset Railway but was visiting the Gloucestershire Warwickshire Railway on 28 July 2018 and is seen at Toddington prior to working to Cheltenham Racecourse. *Pip Dunn*

Class 37

37003	D6703	xot	BRB	LR	UR	
37009	D6709, 37340	xot	BRB	GCN	UR	
37023	D6723	xo	UND	ALL	UR	
37029	D6729	xot	GYP	EOR	OP	
37032	D6732, 37353	xot	GYP	NNR	UR	
37037	D6737, 37321	xip	BRB	SDR	UR	
37042	D6742	xot	EWS	EDR	SU	
37075	D6775	xop	TTG	KWV	OP	
37097	D6797	xo	BRB	CAL	UR	*Old Fettercairn*
37108	D6808, 37325	xip	BRB	RAC	UR	
37109	D6809	xo	BRB	ELR	OP	
37142	D6842	xop	BRB	BWR	OP	
37152	D6852, 37310	xop	UND	PKR	UR	
37190	D6890, 37314	xip	BRB	MRB	UR	
37214	D6914	xot	WCR	BKR	SU	
37215	D6915	xotp	BRB	GWR	OP	
37216	D6916	xotp	GYP	PBR	UR	
37227	D6927	xotp	TLM	CPR	OP	
37240	D6940	xotp	BRB	LLR	OP	
37248	D6948	xbp	GYP	GWR	OP	

Owned by the D05 Preservation Group, ex-DRS 37688 is currently based at the Severn Valley Railway. It is due to lose its DRS blue for Trainload Construction colours and should be renamed *Great Rocks*. It was at Kidderminster on 18 May 2018 waiting to work to Bridgnorth. *Pip Dunn*

37250	D6950	xotp	TRN	WEN	UR	
37261	D6961	aip	DRU	BKR	UR	
37263	D6963	xop	BRB	TSR	UR	
37264	D6964	xip	LLB	NYM	OP	
37275	D6975	xotp	BRB	PDR	OP	
37294	D6994	xotp	BRB	EBR	OP	
37308	D6608, 37274	xotp	UND	DFR	UR	
37350	D6700, 37119	xot	GYP	NRM	UR	
37674	D6869, 37169	xotp	RSR	WEN	OP	
37679	D6823, 37123	xotp	TTG	ELR	SU	
37688	D6905, 37205	aotp	DRU	SVR	OP	
37703	D6767, 37067	xotp	DRU	BKR	OP	
37714	D6724, 37024	xotp	TLM	GCR	OP	*Cardiff Canton*

Class 40

40012	D212, 97407	xi	BRB	ELR	UR	*AUREOL*
40106	D306	vb	GFY	ELR	OP	*ATLANTIC CONVEYOR*
40118	D318, 97408	xi	BRB	TRM	UR	
40122	D200	xi	GNY	NRM	SU	
40135	D335, 97406	xb	BRB	ELR	OP	

Class 41

41001	43000, ADB975812	ae	BRP	GCN	OP	

Class 42

	D821	vi	MYP	SVR	OP	*GREYHOUND*
	D832	vb	GYP	ELR	OP	*ONSLAUGHT*

Class 44

44004	D4	vo	GNY	MRB	OP	*GREAT GABLE*
44008	D8	vo	GYP	PKR	OP	*PENYGHENT*

Class 45

45015	D14	xo	BRB	BAT	SU	
45041	D53	xi	BRB	MRB	OP	*ROYAL TANK REGIMENT*
45060	D100	xi	BRB	BH	OP	*SHERWOOD FORESTER*
45105	D86	xe	BRB	BH	UR	
45108	D120	xe	BRB	ELR	OP	
45112	D61	xe	BRB	BU	SU	*ROYAL ARMY ORDNACE CORPS*
45125	D123	xe	GYP	GCR	OP	*LEICESTERSHIRE AND DERBYSHIRE YEOMANRY*
45132	D22	xe	BRB	EOR	UR	
45133	D40	xe	BRB	NNR	UR	
45135	D99	xe	BRB	ELR	UR	*3RD CARABINIER*
45149	D135	xe	BRB	GWR	OP	

Class 46

46010	D147	xo	BRB	GCN	UR	
46035	D172, 97403	xo	BRB	PKR	SU	
46045	D182, 97404	xb	BYP	MRB	UR	

Now main line registered and hauling charter trains for Saphos Trains, Class 40 D213 *Andania* was a visitor to the North Yorkshire Moors Railway in 2016. On 18 June it waits to work the 1357 Grosmont-Pickering. *Pip Dunn*

Both surviving Class 42 Warship Diesel Hydraulics were reunited at the Severn Valley Railway in 2018 when D832 *Onslaught* visited from the East Lancashire Railway and joined resident D821 *Greyhound*. On May 18, D832 arrives at Highley on the 1518 Bridgnorth-Kidderminster. *Pip Dunn*

Superbly restored in BR blue, 45149 is stabled at Toddington in between duties on 28 July 2018. *Pip Dunn*

Recreating a typical Western Region scene of the late 1970s, BR blue 45041 *Royal Tank Regiment* and 50035 *Ark Royal* stand side-by-side at Kidderminster on 19 May 2018. *Pip Dunn*

47579 *James Nightall GC* leads 31430 *Sister Dora* at the Mangapps Railway Museum in Essex on 27 August 2016. The Class 47 is currently on loan at the Mid Hants Railway, where it has had its vacuum brakes reinstated. *Anthony Hicks*

Class 47

47004	D1524	xip	GYP	EBR	SU	
47105	D1693	xb	BRB	GWR	UR	
47117	D1705	xip	BRB	GCR	OP	*SPARROWHAWK*
47192	D1842	xo	GFY	RAC	OP	
47205	D1855, 47395	xotm	RFD	NLR	OP	
47292	D1994	xotm	BLL	GCN	OP	
47306	D1787	xotm	RFE	BWR	UR	*The Sapper*
47367	D1886	xos	BRB	MNR	OP	*KENNY COCKBIRD*
47376	D1895	xos	FTT	GWR	OP	*Freightliner 1995*
47401	D1500	xe	BRB	MRB	OP	*North Eastern*
47402	D1501	xe	GYP	ELR	OP	
47417	D1516	xei	GYP	MRB	UR	
47449	D1566	xe	BRB	LLR	OP	
47484	D1662	xe	GWR	WIS	UR	*ISAMBARD KINGDOM BRUNEL*
47524	D1107	xe	RES	CHV	UR	
47579	D1778, 47183, 47793	xet	BRE	MHR	OP	*James Nightall GC*
47596	D1933, 47255	xe	NSD	MNR	OP	*Aldeburgh Festival*
47635	D1606, 47029	xe	LLB	EOR	UR	*Jimmy Milne*
47640	D1921, 47244	xe	LLB	BAT	OP	*University of Strathclyde*
47643	D1970, 47269	xep	IOS	BKR	OP	
47712	D1948, 47505	xet	SCR	RAC	OP	*Lady Diana Spencer*
47761	D1619, 47038, 47564	aet	RES	MRB	SU	
47765	D1643, 47059, 47631	xet	SCR	ELR	OP	
47771	D1946, 47503	aet	RES	ZG	UR	
47785	D1909, 47232, 47665, 47820	xet	EWS	WEN	SU	

Back in mid-1980-style ScotRail livery, 47712 *Lady Diana Spencer* has been popular visiting heritage railways in 2018. On 18 May it arrives at Bewdley with the 1206 Bridgnorth-Kidderminster. *Pip Dunn*

47799	D1654, 47070, 47620, 47835	aet	ROY	EDR	SU	*Prince Henry*
47828	D1966, 47266, 47629	aet	ICS	GCN	OP	
47840	D1661, 47077, 47613	xot	BLU	WSR	OP	*NORTH STAR*

Class 50

50002	D402	xep	BRB	SDR	UR	
50015	D415	xep	LLB	ELR	OP	*Valiant*
50019	D419	xep	LLB	MNR	UR	*Ramillies*
50021	D421	xep	LLB	ZG	UR	*Rodney*
50026	D426	xep	NSD	SVR	UR	*Indomitable*
50027	D427	xep	NSR	MHR	OP	*Lion*
50029	D429	xep	LLB	PKR	SU	*Renown*
50030	D430	xep	LLB	PKR	UR	*Repulse*
50031	D431	xep	ICS	SVR	OP	*Hood*
50033	D433	xep	UND	SVR	OP	*Glorious*
50035	D435	xep	BRB	SVR	OP	*Ark Royal*
50042	D442	xep	LLB	BWR	OP	*Triumph*

Class 52

	D1010	xo	MYP	WSR	OP	*WESTERN CAMPAIGNER*
	D1013	xo	BRB	SVR	UR	*WESTERN RANGER*
	D1023	xi	BRB	NRM	SU	*WESTERN FUSILIER*
	D1041	xo	BRB	ELR	UR	*WESTERN PRINCE*
	D1048	xo	BRB	MRB	UR	*WESTERN LADY*
	D1062	xo	BRB	SVR	UR	*WESTERN COURIER*

Based at the Severn Valley Railway, 50035 *Ark Royal* was a guest at the West Somerset Railway in 2018. On 9 June it arrives at Minehead with the 1318 from Bishops Lydeard. *Anthony Hicks*

Class 55

55015	D9015	xe	GYP	BH	UR	*TULYAR*
55019	D9019	xe	BRB	BH	OP	*ROYAL HIGHLAND FUSILIER*

Class 56

56006		aos	BRB	ELR	OP
56097		aos	TLC	GCN	UR

Class 58

58012		aosp	TMF	BAT	SU

Although main line registered, D1015 *Western Champion* has been restricted to heritage lines only in 2018 due to one of its engines being defective. It was at Kidderminster on 19 May prior to working to Bridgnorth. *Pip Dunn*

Part of the National Collection based at York, D9002 *The King's Own Yorkshire Light Infantry* was a visitor to the Severn Valley Railway on 20 May 2016 and waits to work the 1506 Bridgnorth-Kidderminster. This loco is back on display at the NRM. *Pip Dunn*

58016	aosp	FER	LR	UR
58022	aosp	TMF	PKR	SU
58023	aosp	MLB	BAT	UR
58048	aosp	EWS	BAT	SU

Main line electric locos

Last number	Previous official numbers carried	Key detail differences	Livery	Location	Status	Current name
Class 71						
71001	E5001	xe	GYP	NRS	SU	
Class 73						
73001	E6001, 73901	xew	BRB	DFR	OP	
73002	E6002	xew	LLB	DFR	SU	
73003	E6003	xew	GYP	SCR	OP	*Sir Herbert Walker*
73114	E6020	xew	LLB	BAT	UR	
73118	E6024	xewl	EUS	BIR	OP	
73129	E6036	xew	EBP	GWR	OP	
73130	E6037	xewl	EUS	FIN	OP	
73140	E6047	xew	NSR	SPA	OP	
73210	E6022, 73116	xew	IGX	EVR	OP	*Selhurst*

Class 76

| 76020 | E26020 | vo | BLK | NRM | SU | |

Class 77

1502	E27000	ae	BLK	MRB	SU	*ELECTRA*
1505	E27001	ae	DNS	MSIM	SU	*ARIADNE*
1501	E27003	ae	DNS	TIL	OP	*DIANA*

Class 81

| 81002 | E3003 | xe | BRB | BH | SU | |

Class 82

| 82008 | E3054 | xe | ICO | BH | SU | |

Class 83

| 83012 | E3035 | xe | EBY | BH | SU | |

Class 84

| 84001 | E3036 | xe | BRB | BH | SU | |

Class 85

| 85006 | E3061, 85101 | xe | BRB | BH | SU | |

Class 87

| 87001 | | ae | BRB | NRM | SU | *Stephenson* |
| 87035 | | ae | BRB | RAC | UR | *Robert Burns* |

Class 89

| 89001 | | ae | ICO | BH | UR | |

Prototype Type 5 diesel-electric Co-Co

| DP1 | | vi | POW | NRS | SU | *DELTIC* |

Note: the number DP1 was not displayed on the locomotive

Prototype 500hp diesel-electric 0-6-0

| D226 | D0226 | vo | GRE | KWV | OP | |

4 Disposed locomotives

This part of the book lists all locos that were owned or leased by BR and subsequent private TOCs/FOCs but have since been scrapped. They are listed by their last number carried, and all previous numbers are detailed, with the most recent number(s) applied before the last number. Some locos, such as Class 31/5s and 47/8s, carried the same TOPS number twice. Locos owned by the 'Big four' that were withdrawn before nationalisation are not included.

All pre-TOPS numbers on diesels were initially prefixed D, which may or may not have been removed and so are excluded. Any allocated TOPS numbers that were allocated or intended but not applied are not listed.

Industrial shunting locos registered in the 015xx series are not detailed.

Unclassified LMS shunters

	7055
	7056
7408	7058

Unclassified shunter diesel-mechanical 0-4-0

2400	11177
2401	11178
2402	11179
2403	11180
2404	11181
2405	11182
2406	11183
2407	11184
2408	11185
2409	11186

Unclassified shunter diesel-mechanical 0-4-0

2500	11116
2501	11117
2502	11118
2503	11119
2504	11120
2505	11144
2506	11145
2507	11146
2508	11147
2509	11148
2510	
2512	
2513	
2514	
2515	
2516	
2517	
2518	
2519	

Unclassified shunter diesel-hydraulic 0-4-0

2700	11700
2701	11701
2702	11702
2703	11703
2704	11704
2705	11705
2706	11706
2707	11707

Unclassified shunter diesel-hydraulic 0-4-0

2708	11708
2709	11709
2710	11710
2711	11711
2712	11712
2713	11713
2714	11714
2715	11715
2716	11716
2717	11717
2718	11718
2719	11719

2720
2721
2722
2723
2724
2725
2726
2727
2728
2729
2730
2731
2732
2733
2734
2735
2736
2737
2738
2739
2740
2741
2742
2743
2744
2745
2746
2747
2748
2749
2750
2751
2752
2753
2754
2755
2756
2757
2758
2759
2760
2761
2762
2763
2764
2765
2766
2768
2769
2770
2771
2772
2773
2775
2776
2777
2778
2779
2780

Unclassified shunter diesel-hydraulic 0-4-0
2900
2901
2902
2903
2904
2905
2906
2907
2908
2909
2910
2911
2912
2913

Unclassified shunter diesel mechanical 0-4-0

2950	11500
2951	11501
2952	11502

Unclassified shunter diesel-mechanical 0-4-0

2957	11507
2958	11508

Unclassified shunter diesel-electric 0-4-0
2999

Unclassified shunter diesel-electric 0-6-0

3117	13117
3118	13118
3119	13119
3120	13120
3121	13121
3122	13122
3123	13123
3124	13124
3125	13125
3126	13126
3152	1352
3153	1353
3154	1354
3155	1355
3156	1356
3157	1357
3158	1358
3159	1359
3160	1360
3161	1361
3162	1362
3163	1363
3164	1364
3165	1365
3166	1366

Unclassified shunter diesel-mechanical 0-6-0
11104
This was the same design as a Class 04

Unclassified shunter diesel-electric 0-6-0
12000
12001

Unclassified shunter diesel-electric 0-6-0
12002

Unclassified shunter diesel-electric 0-6-0

12003	7080
12004	7081
12005	7082
12006	7083
12007	7084
12008	7085
12009	7086
12010	7087
12011	7088
12012	7089
12013	7090
12014	7091
12015	7092
12016	7093
12017	7094
12018	7095
12019	7096
12020	7097
12021	7098
12022	7099
12023	7110
12024	7111
12025	7112
12026	7113
12027	7114
12028	7115
12029	7116
12030	7117
12031	7118
12032	7119

LNER Unclassified shunter diesel-electric 0-6-0

15000	8000
15001	8001
15002	8002
15003	8003

LNER Unclassified shunter diesel-electric 0-6-0
15004

GWR Unclassified shunter diesel-electric 0-6-0
15100

GWR Unclassified shunter diesel-electric 0-6-0
15101
15102
15103
15104
15105
15106

Unclassified shunter diesel-electric 0-6-0
15107

SR Unclassified shunter diesel-electric 0-6-0
15201
15202
15203

LMS Prototype Type 3 1,600hp diesel-electric Co-Co
10000
10001

Prototype 2,040hp diesel-mechanical 2-D-2
10100

Prototype Type 3 1,750hp diesel-electric 1Co-Co1
10201
10202

Prototype Type 4 2,000hp diesel-electric 1Co-Co1
10203

Prototype Type 1 827hp diesel-electric Bo-Bo
10800

Prototype 500hp Diesel-mechanical 0-6-0
11001

Prototype 500hp diesel-hydraulic 0-6-0

D227	D0227

Prototype Type 4 diesel-electric Co-Co
DP2

Prototype Type 4 diesel-electric Co-Co
0260

Prototype Type 5 diesel-electric Co-Co
HS4000

Various trial locos
D9998
JANUS
TAURUS
VULCAN

Unclassified electric Bo-Bo

26500	6480
26501	6481

Unclassified electric Bo-Bo

26502	6490

26503	6491
26504	6492
26505	6493
26506	6494
26507	6495
26508	6496
26509	6497
26510	6498
26511	6499

Unclassified electric Bo-Bo

26600	6999

Unclassified gas turbine A1A-A1A

E1000	E2000	18100

Unclassified gas turbine 4-6-0

GT3

Class 01 shunter diesel-mechanical 0-4-0

01001	2954	11504
01002	2955	11505
	2956	

Two locos were numbered D2956, this one and the Class 01, which is preserved

Class 02 shunter diesel-hydraulic 0-4-0

	2850
02001	2851
	2852
	2855
02004	2856
	2857
	2859
	2861
	2862
	2863
	2864
	2865
	2869

Class 03 shunter diesel-mechanical 0-6-0

	2000
	2001
	2002
	2003
03004	2004
03005	2005
	2006
03007	2007
03008	2008
03009	2009
03010	2010
	2011
03012	2012
03013	2013
03014	2014
	2015
03016	2016
03017	2017
	2019
03021	2021
03025	2025
03026	2026
	2028
03029	2029
	2030
	2031
	2032
	2033
03034	2034
03035	2035
	2036
	2038
	2039
	2040
	2042
	2043
03044	2044
03045	2045
03047	2047
	2048
03050	2049
	2050
	2052
	2053
	2054
03055	2055
03056	2056
	2057
03058	2058
03060	2060
03061	2061
03064	2064
	2065
03067	2067
03068	2068
	2070
	2071
	2074
03075	2075
03076	2076
	2077
03080	2080
	2082
	2083
	2085
03086	2086
	2087
	2088
03091	2091
03092	2092
	2093
03095	2095
03096	2096
03097	2097
03098	2098
	2100
	2101
03102	2102
03103	2103
03104	2104
03105	2105
03106	2106
03107	2107
03108	2108
03109	2109
03110	2110
03111	2111
	2114
	2115
	2116
03121	2121
	2122
	2123
	2124
	2125
	2126
	2127
03129	2129
	2130
	2131
	2132
03135	2135
	2136
03137	2137
	2140
03142	2142
	2143
	2146
03147	2147
03149	2149
	2150
03151	2151
03153	2153
03154	2154
03155	2155
03157	2157
03159	2159
03160	2160
03161	2161
03163	2163

03164	2164	2230	11149
03165	2165	2231	11150
03166	2166	2232	11151
03167	2167	2233	11152
03168	2168	2234	11153
03169	2169	2235	11154
03171	2171	2236	11155
03172	2172	2237	11156
	2173	2238	11157
03174	2174	2239	11158
03175	2175	2240	11159
	2176	2241	11160
	2177	2242	11212
	2181	2243	11213
	2183	2244	11214
	2185	2247	11217
	2186	2248	11218
	2187	2249	11219
	2188	2250	11220
	2190	2251	11221
	2191	2252	11222
	2193	2253	11223
	2194	2254	11224
	2195	2255	11225
	2198	2256	11226
03370	2370	2257	11227
	2372	2258	11228
	2373	2259	11229
	2374	2260	
	2375	2261	
	2376	2262	
	2377	2263	
	2378	2264	
	2379	2265	
	2380	2266	
03382	2382	2267	
	2383	2268	
	2384	2269	
	2385	2270	
03386	2386	2273	
	2387	2274	
	2388	2275	
03389	2389	2276	
	2390	2277	
	2391	2278	
	2392	2281	
	2393	2282	
	2394	2283	
	2395	2285	
	2396	2286	
03397	2397	2287	
	2398	2288	

Class 04 shunter diesel-mechanical 0-6-0

2200	11100	2290	
2201	11101	2291	
2202	11102	2292	
2204	11105	2293	
2206	11107	2294	
2208	11109	2295	
2209	11110	2296	
2210	11111	2297	
2211	11112	2298	
2212	11113	2299	
2213	11114	2300	
2214	11115	2301	
2215	11121	2303	
2216	11122	2304	
2217	11123	2305	
2218	11124	2306	
2219	11125	2307	
2220	11126	2308	
2221	11127	2309	
2222	11128	2311	
2223	11129	2312	
2224	11130	2313	
2225	11131	2314	
2226	11132	2315	
2227	11133	2316	
2228	11134	2317	
		2318	
		2319	

2320	
2321	
2322	
2323	
2326	
2327	
2328	
2329	
2330	
2331	
2332	
2333	
2335	
2336	
2338	
2339	
2340	
2341	S1173

Class 05 shunter diesel-mechanical 0-6-0

2550	11136
2551	11137
2552	11138
2553	11139
2555	11141
2556	11142
2557	11143
2558	11161
2559	11162
2560	11163
2561	11164
2562	11165
2563	11166
2564	11167
2565	11168
2566	11169
2567	11170
2568	11171
2569	11172
2570	11173
2571	11174
2572	11175
2573	11176
2574	
2575	
2576	
2577	
2579	
2580	
2581	
2582	
2583	
2584	
2585	
2586	
2588	
2589	
2590	
2591	
2592	
2593	
2594	
2596	
2597	
2598	
2599	
2600	
2601	
2602	
2603	
2604	
2605	
2606	
2607	
2608	
2609	
2610	
2611	
2612	
2613	

2614	
2615	
2616	
2617	
2618	

Class 06 shunter diesel-mechanical 0-4-0

	2410
	2411
	2412
06001	2413
06002	2414
	2415
	2416
	2417
	2418
	2419
06004	2421
06005	2422
06006	2423
	2424
	2425
06007	2426
	2427
	2428
	2429
	2430
	2431
	2432
	2433
	2434
	2435
	2436
06008	2437
	2438
	2439
06009	2440
	2441
	2442
	2443
06010	2444

Class 07 shunter diesel-electric 0-6-0

07002	2986
07003	2987
	2988
07006	2990
	2992
07009	2993
	2998

Class 08 shunter diesel-electric 0-6-0

	3001	13001
	3003	13003
08001	3004	13004
08002	3005	13005
ADB966507	3006	13006
08003	3007	13007
08004	3008	13008
08005	3009	13009
08006	3010	13010
	3011	13011
	3012	13012
	3013	13013
08008	3015	13015
08009	3016	13016
08010	3017	13017
	3020	13020
08014	3021	13021
	3024	13024
08018	3025	13025
	3026	13026
08019	3027	13027
	3028	13028
08023	3031	13031
08024	3032	13032
08025	3033	13033
	3034	13034
ADB966508	3035	13035
08026	3036	13036
ADB966510	3037	13037

	3038	13038	08101	3136	13136	
08027	3039	13039	08103	3168	13168	
08028	3040	13040	08104	3169	13169	
08029	3041	13041	08105	3170	13170	
08030	3042	13042	08106	3171	13171	
08031	3043	13043		3172	13172	
	3045	13045	08107	3173	13173	
08033	3046	13046	08109	3175	13175	
08035	3048	13048	08110	3176	13176	
08036	3049	13049	08111	3177	13177	ADB966512
08037	3050	13050	08112	3178	13178	
	3051	13051	08113	3179	13179	
	3052	13052	08115	3181	13181	
	3053	13053	08116	3182	13182	
08041	3054	13054		3183	13183	
08042	3055	13055	08117	3184	13184	ADB966513
08043	3056	13056	08118	3185	13185	
08044	3057	13057	08119	3186	13186	ADB966511
08045	3058	13058	08120	3187	13187	
08047	3060	13060	08121	3188	13188	
08048	3061	13061	08122	3189	13189	
08049	3062	13062	08124	3191	13191	
08050	3063	13063	08125	3192	13192	
08051	3064	13064		3193	13193	
08052	3065	13065	08126	3194	13194	
08053	3066	13066	08127	3195	13195	
08055	3068	13068	08128	3196	13196	
ADB966509	3069	13069	08129	3197	13197	
08056	3070	13070	08130	3198	13198	
08057	3071	13071	08131	3199	13199	
08058	3072	13072	08132	3200	13200	
08059	3073	13073	08134	3202	13202	
08061	3075	13075	08135	3203	13203	
08062	3076	13076	08136	3204	13204	
08063	3077	13077	08137	3205	13205	
ADB966506	3078	13078	08138	3206	13206	
08065	3080	13080	08139	3207	13207	
08066	3081	13081	08140	3208	13208	
08067	3082	13082	08141	3209	13209	
08068	3083	13083	08142	3210	13210	
08069	3084	13084	08143	3211	13211	
08070	3085	13085	08144	3212	13212	
08071	3086	13086	08145	3213	13213	
	3087	13087	08146	3214	13214	
	3088	13088	08147	3215	13215	
08074	3089	13089	08148	3216	13216	
08075	3090	13090	08149	3217	13217	
08076	3091	13091	08150	3218	13218	
	3093	13093	08151	3219	13219	
	3094	13094	08152	3220	13220	
	3095	13095	08153	3221	13221	
	3096	13096	08154	3222	13222	
	3097	13097	08155	3223	13223	
	3098	13098	08156	3224	13224	
	3099	13099	08157	3225	13225	
	3100	13100	08158	3226	13226	
08077	3102	13102	08159	3227	13227	
08078	3103	13103	08160	3228	13228	
08079	3104	13104	08161	3229	13229	
08080	3105	13105	08162	3230	13230	
08081	3106	13106	08163	3231	13231	
08082	3107	13107	08165	3233	13233	
08083	3108	13108	08166	3234	13234	
08084	3109	13109	08167	3235	13235	
08085	3110	13110	08169	3237	13237	
08086	3111	13111	08170	3238	13238	
08087	3112	13112	08171	3239	13239	
08088	3113	13113	08172	3240	13240	
08089	3114	13114	08173	3241	13241	PO1
08090	3115	13115	08174	3242	13242	
08091	3116	13116	08175	3243	13243	
08092	3127	13127	08176	3244	13244	
08093	3128	13128	08177	3245	13245	
08094	3129	13129	08178	3246	13246	
08095	3130	13130	08179	3247	13247	
08096	3131	13131	08180	3248	13248	
08097	3132	13132	08181	3249	13249	
08098	3133	13133	08182	3250	13250	
08099	3134	13134	08183	3251	13251	
08100	3135	13135	08184	3252	13252	

08185	3253	13253			08271	3341	13341
08186	3254	13254			08272	3342	13342
08187	3256	13256			08273	3343	13343
08188	3257	13257			08274	3344	13344
08189	3258	13258			08275	3345	13345
08190	3259	13259			08276	3346	13346
08191	3260	13260			08277	3347	13347
08192	3262	13262			08278	3348	13348
08193	3263	13263			08279	3349	13349
08194	3264	13264			08280	3350	13350
08196	3266	13266			08281	3351	13351
08197	3267	13267			08282	3352	13352
08198	3268	13268			08283	3353	13353
08199	3269	13269			08284	3354	13354
08200	3270	13270			08285	3355	13355
08201	3271	13271			08286	3356	13356
08204	3274	13274			08287	3357	13357
08205	3275	13275			08289	3359	
08206	3276	13276			08290	3360	
08207	3277	13277			08291	3361	
08208	3278	13278			08292	3362	13362
08209	3279	13279			08293	3363	13363
08210	3280	13280			08294	3364	13364
08211	3281	13281			08295	3365	13365
08212	3282	13282			08296	3366	13366
08213	3283	13283			08297	3367	
08214	3284	13284			08298	3368	
08215	3285	13285			08299	3369	
08216	3286	13286			08300	3370	
08217	3287	13287			08301	3371	
08218	3288	13288			08302	3372	
08219	3289	13289			08303	3373	
08221	3291	13291			08304	3374	
08222	3292	13292			08305	3375	
08223	3293	13293			08306	3376	
08224	3294	13294			08307	3377	
08225	3295	13295			08309	3379	
08226	3296	13296			08310	3380	
08227	3297	13297			08311	3381	
08228	3298	13298			08312	3382	
08229	3299	13299			08313	3383	
08230	3300	13300			08314	3384	
08231	3301	13301			08315	3385	
08232	3302	13302			08316	3386	
08233	3303	13303			08317	3387	
08234	3304	13304			08318	3388	
08235	3305	13305			08319	3389	
08236	3306	13306			08320	3390	
08237	3307	13307			08321	3391	
08239	3309	13309			08322	3392	
08240	3310	13310			08323	3393	
08241	3311	13311			08324	3394	
08242	3312	13312			08325	3395	
08243	3313	13313			08326	3396	
08244	3314	13314			08327	3397	
08245	3315	13315			08328	3398	
08246	3316	13316			08329	3399	
08247	3317	13317	PO1		08330	3400	
08248	3318	13318			08332	3402	
08249	3319	13319			08333	3403	
08250	3320	13320			08334	3404	
08251	3321	13321			08335	3405	
08252	3322	13322			08336	3406	
08253	3323	13323			08337	3407	
08254	3324	13324			08338	3408	
08255	3325	13325			08339	3409	
08256	3326	13326			08340	3410	
08257	3327	13327			08341	3411	
08258	3328	13328			08342	3412	
08260	3330	13330			08343	3413	
08261	3331	13331			08344	3414	
08262	3332	13332			08345	3415	
08263	3333	13333			08346	3416	
08264	3334	13334			08347	3417	
08265	3335	13335			08348	3418	
08267	97801	RDB968020	3337		08349	3419	
	13337				08350	3420	
08268	3338	13338			08351	3421	
08269	3339	13339			08352	3422	
08270	3340	13340			08353	3423	

08354	3424	08456	3571
08355	3425	08457	3572
08356	3426	08458	3573
08357	3427	08459	3574
08358	3428	08461	3576
08360	3430	08463	3578
08361	3431	08464	3579
08362	3432	08465	3580
08363	3433	08466	3581
08364	3434	08467	3582
08365	3435	08468	3583
08366	3436	08469	3584
08367	3437	08470	3585
08368	3438	08474	3589
08369	3454	08475	3590
08370	3455	08477	3592
08371	3456	08478	3593
08372	3457	08481	3596
08373	3458	08482	3597
08374	3459	08486	3601
08376	3461	08487	3602
08378	3463	08488	3603
08379	3464	08489	3604
08380	3465	08491	3606
08381	3466	08492	3607
08382	3467	08493	3608
08383	3468	08494	3609
08384	3469	08496	3611
08385	3470	08497	3652
08386	3471	08498	3653
08387	3472	08501	3656
08388	3503	08504	3659
08390	3505	08505	3660
08391	3506	08506	3661
08392	3507	08508	3663
08393	3508	08509	3664
08394	3509	08510	3672
08395	3510	08512	3674
08396	3511	08513	3675
08397	3512	08514	3676
08398	3513	08515	3677
08399	3514	08517	3679
08400	3515	08518	3680
08402	3517	08519	3681
08403	3518	08520	3682
08404	3519	08521	3683
08406	3521	08522	3684
08407	3522	08524	3686
08408	3523	08526	3688
08409	3524	08529	3691
08412	3527	08532	3694
08413	3528	08533	3695
08414	3529	08534	3696
08415	3530	08535	3699
08416	3531	08537	3701
08419	3534	08538	3702
08420	3535	08539	3703
08422	3537	08540	3704
08424	3539	08541	3705
08425	3540	08542	3706
08426	3541	08543	3707
08427	3542	08544	3708
08429	3544	08545	3709
08430	3545	08546	3710
08431	3546	08547	3711
08432	3547	08548	3712
08433	3548	08549	3713
08434	3549	08550	3714
08435	3550	08551	3715
08437	3552	08552	3716
08438	3553	08553	3717
08439	3554	08554	3718
08440	3555	08555	3722
08446	3561	08557	3724
08448	3563	08558	3725
08449	3564	08559	3726
08450	3565	08560	3727
08452	3567	08561	3728
08453	3568	08562	3729
08455	3570	08563	3730

08564	3731	08699	3866
08565	3732	08702	3869
08566	3733	08705	3872
08569	3736	08707	3874
08570	3737	08708	3875
08572	3739	08710	3877
08574	3741	08712	3879
08576	3743	08713	3880
08577	3744	08715	3882
08579	3746	08716	3883
08581	3748		3885
08582	3749	08718	3886
08583	3750	08719	3887
08584	3751	08720	3888
08586	3753	08722	3890
08587	3754	08723	3891
08589	3756	08725	3893
08591	3758	08726	3894
08594	3761	08727	3895
08595	3762	08728	3896
08597	3764	08729	3897
08599	3766	08731	3899
08601	3768	08733	3901
08603	3770	08734	3902
08606	3773	08736	3904
08607	3774	08739	3907
08608	3775	08740	3908
08609	3776	08741	3909
08610	3777	08744	3912
08612	3779	08745	3913
08614	3781	08746	3914
08618	3785	08747	3915
08619	3786	08748	3916
08621	3788	08751	3919
08625	3792	08753	3921
08626	3793	08755	3923
08627	3794	08758	3926
08628	3795	08760	3928
08634	3801	08761	3929
08636	3803	08763	3931
08637	3805	08768	3936
08638	3805	08770	3938
08639	3806	08771	3939
08640	3807	08775	3943
08642	3809	08776	3944
08646	3813	08777	3945
08647	3814	08778	3946
08651	3818	08779	3947
08654	3821	08789	3957
08655	3822	08791	3959
08656	3823	08792	3960
08657	3824	08793	3961
08658	3825	08794	3962
08659	3826	08796	3964
08660	3827	08797	3965
08661	3828	08800	3968
08662	3829	08801	3969
08664	3831	08803	3971
08665	3832	08806	3974
08666	3833	08807	3975
08667	3834	08808	3976
08668	3835	08811	3979
08671	3838	08812	3980
08672	3839	08813	3981
08673	3840	08814	3982
08674	3841	08815	3983
08675	3842	08816	3984
08677	3844	08817	3985
08679	3846	08819	3987
08680	3847	08820	3988
08681	3848	08821	3989
08684	3851	08826	3994
08686	3853	08827	3995
08688	3855	08828	3996
08689	3856	08829	3997
08692	3859	08831	3999
08693	3860	08837	4005
08695	3862	08838	4006
08697	3864	08839	4007
08698	3865	08840	4008

08841	4009	
08842	4010	
08843	4011	
08844	4012	
08848	4016	
08849	4017	
08851	4019	
08852	4020	
08854	4022	
08855	4023	
08856	4024	
08857	4025	
08858	4026	
08859	4027	
08860	4028	
08861	4029	
08862	4030	
08863	4031	
08864	4032	
08866	4034	
08867	4035	
08869	4037	
08875	4043	
08876	4044	
08878	4046	
08880	4048	
08882	4096	
08883	4097	
08884	4098	
08886	4116	
08889	4119	
08890	4120	
08893	4123	
08894	4124	
08895	4125	
08897	4127	
08898	4128	
08900	4130	
08901	4131	
08902	4132	
08906	4136	
08909	4139	
08910	4140	
08914	4144	
08916	4146	
08917	4147	
08919	4149	
08920	4150	
08923	4153	
08926	4156	
08928	4158	
08929	4159	
08930	4160	
08931	4161	
08932	4162	
08935	4165	
08938	4168	
08940	4170	
08941	4171	
08942	4172	
08945	4175	
08946	4176	
08949	4179	
08951	4181	
08952	4182	
08953	4183	
08955	4185	
08957	4191	
08958	4192	
08991	3273	08203
08992	3329	08259

Class 09 shunter diesel-electric 0-6-0

09003	3667	
09005	3669	
09008	3719	
09011	4099	
09013	4101	
09016	97806	4104
09020	4108	
09021	4109	
09101	08833	4001
09102	08832	4000
09103	08766	3934
09104	08749	3917
09105	08835	4003
09202	08732	3900
09203	08781	3949
09205	08620	3787

Class 10 shunter diesel-electric 0-6-0

3137	13137
3138	13138
3139	13139
3140	13140
3141	13141
3142	13142
3143	13143
3144	13144
3145	13145
3146	13146
3147	13147
3148	13148
3149	13149
3150	13150
3151	13151
3439	
3440	
3441	
3442	
3443	
3444	
3445	
3446	
3447	
3448	
3449	
3450	
3451	
3453	
3473	
3474	
3475	
3476	
3477	
3478	
3479	
3480	
3481	
3482	
3483	
3484	
3485	
3486	
3487	
3488	
3490	
3491	
3492	
3493	
3494	
3495	
3496	
3497	
3498	
3499	
3500	
3501	
3502	
3612	
3613	
3614	
3615	
3616	
3617	
3618	
3619	
3620	
3621	
3622	

3623	
3624	
3625	
3626	
3627	
3628	
3629	
3630	
3631	
3632	
3633	
3634	
3635	
3636	
3637	
3638	
3639	
3640	
3641	
3642	
3643	
3644	
3645	
3646	
3647	
3648	
3649	
3650	
3651	
4049	
4050	
4051	
4052	
4053	
4054	
4055	
4056	
4057	
4058	
4059	
4060	
4061	
4062	
4063	
4064	
4065	
4066	
4068	
4069	
4070	
4071	
4072	
4073	
4074	
4075	
4076	
4077	
4078	
4079	
4080	
4081	
4082	
4083	
4084	
4085	
4086	
4087	
4088	
4089	
4090	
4091	
4093	
4094	

Class 11 shunter diesel-electric 0-6-0

12033	7120
12034	7121
12035	7122
12036	7123
12037	7124

12038	7125
12039	7126
12040	7127
12041	7128
12042	7129
12043	7130
12044	7131
12045	
12046	
12047	
12048	
12049	
12050	
12051	
12053	
12054	
12055	
12056	
12057	
12058	
12059	
12060	
12061	
12062	
12063	
12064	
12065	
12066	
12067	
12068	
12069	
12070	
12071	
12072	
12073	
12074	
12075	
12076	
12078	
12079	
12080	
12081	
12084	
12085	
12086	
12087	
12089	
12090	
12091	
12092	
12094	
12095	
12096	
12097	
12098	
12100	
12101	
12102	
12103	
12104	
12105	
12106	
12107	
12108	
12109	
12110	
12111	
12112	
12113	
12114	
12115	
12116	
12117	
12118	
12119	
12120	
12121	
12122	
12123	
12124	

12125
12126
12127
12128
12129
12130
12132
12133
12134
12135
12136
12137
12138

Class 12 shunter diesel-electric 0-6-0
15211
15212
15213
15214
15215
15216
15217
15218
15219
15220
15221
15222
15223
15225
15226
15227
15228
15229
15230
15231
15232
15233
15234
15235
15236

Class 13 shunter diesel-electric 0-6-0+0-6-0

13001	4501	(4189 + 4190)
13002	4502	(4187 + 3697)
13003	4500	(4188 + 3698)

Class 14 Type 1 diesel-hydraulic 0-6-0
9501
9503
9505
9506
9507
9508
9509
9510
9511
9512
9514
9515
9517
9519
9522
9527
9528
9530
9532
9533
9534
9535
9536
9538
9540
9541
9542
9543
9544
9545
9546
9547
9548
9549

9550
9552
9554

Class 15 Type 1 diesel-electric Bo-Bo

8200	
8201	
8202	
8203	DB968003
8204	
8205	
8206	
8207	
8208	
8209	
8210	
8211	
8212	
8213	
8214	
8215	
8216	
8217	
8218	
8219	
8220	
8221	
8222	
8223	
8224	
8225	
8226	
8227	
8228	
8229	
8230	
8231	
8232	
8234	
8235	
8236	
8237	DB968002
8238	
8239	
8240	
8241	
8242	
8243	DB968000

Class 16 Type 1 diesel-electric Bo-Bo
8400
8401
8402
8403
8404
8405
8406
8407
8408
8409

Class 17 Type 1 diesel-electric Bo-Bo
8500
8501
8502
8503
8504
8505
8506
8507
8508
8509
8510
8511
8512
8513
8514
8515
8516
8517
8518

8519
8520
8521   S18521
8522
8523
8524
8525
8526
8527
8528
8529
8530
8531
8532
8533
8534
8535
8536
8537
8538
8539
8540
8541
8542
8543
8544
8545
8546
8547
8548
8549
8550
8551
8552
8553
8554
8555
8556
8557
8558
8559
8560
8561
8562
8563
8564
8565
8566
8567
8569
8570
8571
8572
8573
8574
8575
8576
8577
8578
8579
8580
8581
8582
8583
8584
8585
8586
8587
8588
8589
8590
8591
8592
8593
8594
8595
8596
8597
8598
8599

8600
8601
8602
8603
8604
8605
8606
8607
8608
8609
8610
8611
8612
8613
8614
8615
8616

Class 20 Type 1 diesel-electric Bo-Bo

20002	8002	
20003	8003	
20004	8004	
20005	8005	
20006	8006	
20008	8008	
20009	8009	
20010	8010	
20011	8011	
20012	8012	
20013	8013	
20014	8014	
20015	8015	
20017	8017	
20018	8018	
20019	8019	
20021	8021	
20022	8022	
20023	20301	8023
20024	8024	
20025	8025	
20026	8026	
20027	8027	
20028	8028	
20029	8029	
20030	8030	
20032	8032	
20033	8033	
20034	8034	
20035	8035	CFD2001
20036	8036	
20037	8037	
20038	8038	
20039	8039	
20040	8040	
20043	8043	
20044	8044	
20045	8045	
20046	8046	
20049	8049	
20051	8051	
20052	8052	
20053	8053	
20054	8054	
20055	8055	
20058	8058	
20061	8061	
20062	8062	
20064	8064	
20065	8065	
20067	8067	
20068	8068	
20070	8070	
20071	8071	
20072	8072	
20073	8073	
20074	8074	
20076	8076	
20077	8077	
20078	8078	
20079	8079	

20080	8080	
20082	8082	
20085	8085	
20086	8086	
20089	8089	
20090	8090	
20091	8091	
20092	8092	
20093	8093	
20094	8094	
20097	8097	
20099	8099	
20100	8100	
20103	8103	
20105	8105	
20106	8106	
20108	8108	
20109	8109	
20111	8111	
20112	8112	
20113	8113	
20114	8114	
20115	8115	
20116	8116	
20119	8119	
20122	8122	
20123	8123	
20124	8124	
20125	8125	
20126	8126	
20129	8129	
20130	8130	
20133	8133	
20134	20303	8134
20135	8135	
20136	8136	
20138	8138	
20139	8139	CFD2003
20140	8140	
20141	8141	
20143	8143	
20144	8144	
20145	8145	
20146	8146	
20147	8147	
20148	8148	
20149	8149	
20150	8150	
20151	8151	
20152	8152	
20153	8153	
20155	8155	
20156	8156	
20157	8157	
20158	8158	
20159	8159	
20160	8160	
20161	8161	
20162	8162	
20163	8163	
20164	8164	
20165	8165	
20167	8167	
20170	8170	
20171	8171	
20172	20305	8172
20173	20306	8173
20174	8174	
20175	8175	
20176	8176	
20177	8177	
20178	8178	
20179	8179	
20180	8180	
20181	8181	
20182	8182	
20183	8183	
20184	8184	
20185	8185	
20186	8186	

20191	8191		
20192	8192		
20193	8193		
20195	8195		
20196	20308	8196	
20197	8197		
20198	8198		
20199	8199		
20200	8300		
20201	8301		
20202	8302		
20203	8303		
20204	8304		
20206	8306		
20207	8307		
20208	8308		
20209	8309		
20210	8310		
20211	8311		
20212	8312		
20213	8313		
20215	8315		
20216	8316		
20217	8317		
20218	8318		
20220	8320		
20221	8321		
20222	8322		
20223	8323		
20224	8324		
20226	8326		
20306	20131	8131	
20307	20128	8050	
20310	20190	8190	
20313	20194	20307	8194
20315	20104	8104	
20902	20060	8060	

Note: Numbers 20301-308 were used twice

Class 21 Type 2 diesel-electric Bo-Bo
6104
6105
6109
6110
6111
6115
6117
6118
6120
6122
6125
6126
6127
6128
6131
6134
6135
6136
6138
6139
6140
6141
6142
6143
6144
6145
6146
6147
6148
6149
6150
6151
6152
6153
6154
6155
6156
6157

Class 22 Type 2 diesel-hydraulic B-B

6300
6301
6302
6303
6304
6305
6306
6307
6308
6309
6310
6311
6312
6313
6314
6315
6316
6317
6318
6319
6320
6321
6322
6323
6324
6325
6326
6327
6328
6329
6330
6331
6332
6333
6334
6335
6336
6337
6338
6339
6340
6341
6342
6343
6344
6345
6346
6347
6348
6349
6350
6351
6352
6353
6354
6355
6356
6357

Class 23 Type 2 diesel-electric Bo-Bo

5900
5901
5902
5903
5904
5905
5906
5907
5908
5909

Class 24 Type 2 diesel-electric Bo-Bo

24001	5001
24002	5002
24003	5003
24004	5004
	5005
24005	5000
24006	5006
24007	5007
24008	5008
24009	5009
24010	5010
24011	5011
24012	5012
24013	5013
24014	5014
24015	5015
24016	5016
24017	5017
24018	5018
24019	5019
24020	5020
24021	5021
24022	5022
24023	5023
24024	5024
24025	5025
24026	5026
24027	5027
	5028
24029	5029
24030	5030
24031	5031
24033	5033
24034	5034
24035	5035
24036	5036
24037	5037
24038	5038
24039	5039
24040	5040
24041	5041
24042	5042
	5043
24044	5044
24045	5045
24046	5046
24047	5047
24048	5048
24049	5049
24050	5050
	5051
24052	5052
24053	5053
24055	5055
24056	5056
24057	5057
24058	5058
24059	5059
24060	5060
24062	5062
24063	5063
24064	5064
24065	5065
24066	5066
	5067
	5068
24069	5069
24070	5070
24071	5071
24072	5072
24073	5073
24074	5074
24075	5075
24076	5076
24077	5077
24078	5078
24079	5079
24080	5080
24082	5082
24083	5083
24084	5084
24085	5085
24086	5086
24087	5087
	5088
24089	5089
24090	5090
24091	5091

24092	5092		25020	5170
	5093		25021	5171
24094	5094		25022	5172
24095	5095		25023	5173
24096	5096		25024	5174
24097	5097		25025	5175
24098	5098		25026	5176
24099	5099		25027	5177
24100	5100		25028	5178
24101	5101		25029	5179
24102	5102		25030	5180
24103	5103		25031	5181
24104	5104		25032	5182
24105	5105		25033	5183
24106	5106		25034	5184
24107	5107		25036	5186
24108	5108		25037	5187
24109	5109		25038	5188
24110	5110		25039	5189
24111	5111		25040	5180
24112	5112		25041	5191
24113	5113		25042	5192
	5114		25043	5193
24115	5115		25044	5194
24116	5116		25045	5195
24117	5117		25046	5196
24118	5118		25047	5197
24119	5119		25048	5198
24120	5120		25049	5199
24121	5121		25050	5200
	5122		25051	5201
24123	5123		25052	5202
24124	5124		25053	5203
24125	5125		25054	5204
24126	5126		25055	5205
24127	5127		25056	5206
24128	5128		25058	5208
24129	5129		25060	5210
24130	5130		25061	5211
	5131		25062	5212
24132	5132		25063	5213
24133	5133		25064	5214
24134	5134		25065	5215
24135	5135		25066	5216
24136	5136		25068	5218
24137	5137		25069	5219
	5138		25070	5220
	5139		25071	5221
24140	5140		25073	5223
24141	5141		25074	5224
24142	5142	TDB968009	25075	5225
24143	5143		25076	5226
24144	5144		25077	5227
24145	5145		25078	5228
24146	5146		25079	5229
24147	5147		25080	5230
24148	5148		25081	5231
	5149		25082	5232
24150	5150		25084	5234

Class 25 Type 2 diesel-electric Bo-Bo

25001	5151		25085	5235
25002	5152		25086	5236
25003	5153		25087	5237
25004	5154		25088	5238
25005	5155		25089	5239
25006	5156		25090	5240
25007	5157		25091	5241
25008	5158		25092	5242
25009	5159		25093	5243
25010	5160		25094	5244
25011	5161		25095	5245
25012	5162		25096	5246
25013	5163		25097	5247
25014	5164		25098	5248
25015	5165		25099	5249
25016	5166		25100	5250
25017	5167		25101	5251
25018	5168		25102	5252
25019	5169		25103	5253
			25104	5254
			25105	5255

25106	5256		25192	7542
25107	5257		25193	7543
25108	5258		25194	7544
25109	5259		25195	7545
25110	5260		25196	7546
25111	5261		25197	7547
25112	5262		25198	7548
25113	5263		25199	7549
25114	5264		25200	7550
25115	5265		25201	7551
25116	5266		25202	7552
25117	5267		25203	7553
25118	5268		25204	7554
25119	5269		25205	7555
25120	5270		25206	7556
25121	5271		25207	7557
25122	5272		25208	7558
25123	5273		25209	7559
25124	5274		25210	7560
25125	5275		25211	7561
25126	5276		25212	7562
25127	5277		25213	7563
	5278		25214	7564
25129	5279		25215	7565
25130	5280		25216	7566
25131	5281	97202	25217	7567
25132	5282		25218	7568
25133	5283		25219	7569
25134	5284		25220	7570
25135	5285		25221	7571
25136	5286		25222	7572
25137	5287		25223	7573
25138	5288		25224	7574
25139	5289		25225	7575
25140	5290		25226	7576
25141	5291		25227	7577
25142	5292		25228	7578
25143	5293		25229	7579
25144	5294		25230	7580
25145	5295		25231	7581
25146	5296		25232	7582
25147	5297		25233	7583
25148	5298		25234	7584
25149	5299		25236	7586
25150	7500		25237	7587
25151	7501		25238	7588
25152	7502		25239	7589
25153	7503		25240	7590
25154	7504		25241	7591
25155	7505		25242	7592
25156	7506		25243	7593
25157	7507		25245	7595
25158	7508		25246	7596
25159	7509		25247	7597
25160	7510		25248	7598
25161	7511		25249	7599
25162	7512		25250	7600
25163	7513		25251	7601
25164	7514		25252	7602
25165	7515		25253	7603
25166	7516		25254	7604
25167	7517			7605
25168	7518		25256	7606
25169	7519		25257	7607
25170	7520		25258	7608
25171	7521		25259	7609
25172	7522		25260	7610
25174	7524		25261	7611
25175	7525		25263	7613
25176	7526		25264	7614
25177	7527		25266	7616
25178	7528		25267	7617
25179	7529		25269	7619
25180	7530		25270	7620
25181	7531		25271	7621
25182	7532		25272	7622
25183	7533		25273	7623
25184	7534		25274	7624
25186	7536		25275	7625
25187	7537		25277	7627
25188	7538		25280	7630
25189	7539		25281	7631
25190	7540		25282	7632

25284	7634	
25285	7635	
25287	7637	
25288	7638	
25289	7639	
25290	7640	
25291	7641	
25292	7642	
25293	7643	
25294	7644	
25295	7645	
25298	7648	
25299	7649	
25300	7650	
25301	7651	
25302	7652	
25303	7653	
25304	7654	
25305	7655	97251
25306	7656	
25308	7658	
25310	7660	97250
25311	7661	
25312	7662	
25314	7664	97252
25317	7667	
25318	7668	
25319	7669	
25320	7670	
25321	7671	
25323	7673	
25324	7674	
25325	7675	
25326	7676	
25327	7677	
25902	25268	7618
25903	25276	7626
25905	25286	7636
25906	25296	7646
25907	25297	7647
25908	25307	7657
25910	25315	7665
25911	25316	7666

Class 26 Type 2 diesel-electric Bo-Bo

26003	5303
26005	5305
26006	5306
26008	5308
26009	5309
26012	5312
26013	5313
26015	5315
26016	5316
26017	5317
26018	5318
26019	5319
26020	5307
26021	5321
26022	5322
26023	5323
26026	5326
26027	5327
	5328
26028	5320
26029	5329
26030	5330
26031	5331
26032	5332
26033	5333
26034	5334
26036	5336
26037	5337
26039	5339
26041	5341
26042	5342
26044	5344
26045	5345
26046	5346

Class 27 Type 2 diesel-electric Bo-Bo

27002	5348
27003	5349
27004	5350
27006	5352
27008	5354
27009	5355
27010	5356
27011	5357
27012	5358
27013	5359
27014	5360
27015	5361
27016	5362
27017	5363
27018	5364
27019	5365
27020	5366
27021	5367
27022	5368
27023	5369
27025	5371
27026	5372
27027	5373
27028	5375
27029	5376
27030	5377
27031	5378
27032	5379
27033	5381
27034	5382
	5383
27035	5384
27036	5385
27037	5389
27038	5390
27039	5398
27040	5402
27041	5405
27042	5406
27043	5414
27044	5415

27045	27101	5374	
27046	27102	5380	
27047	27103	27118	5413
27048	27104	5387	
27049	27105	5388	
27051	27107	5395	
27052	27108	5396	
27053	27109	5397	
27054	27110	5399	
27055	27111	5400	
27058	27204	27122	5403
27063	27209	27115	5408
27064	27210	27116	5409
27065	27211	27117	5411
27201	27119	5391	
27202	27120	5392	
27203	27121	5393	
27206	27124	5412	
27207	27113	5404	ADB968025
27208	27114	5407	

Note: Number 27103 was used twice

Class 28 Type 2 diesel-electric Co-Bo

5700
5701
5702
5703
5704
5706
5707
5708
5709
5710
5711
5712
5713
5714
5715
5716
5717
5718
5719

Class 29 Type 2 diesel-electric Bo-Bo

6100
6101
6102
6103
6106
6107
6108
6112
6113
6114
6116
6119
6121
6123
6124
6129
6130
6132
6133
6137

Class 31 Type 2 diesel-electric A1A-A1A

31001	5501	
31002	5502	ADB968014
31003	5503	
31004	5504	
31005	5505	
31006	5506	
31007	5507	
31008	5508	ADB968016
31009	5509	
31010	5510	
31011	5511	
31012	5512	
31013	5513	ADB968013
31014	5514	ADB968015
31015	5515	
31016	5516	
31017	5517	
31019	5519	
31102	5520	
31103	5521	
31107	5525	
31109	5527	
31110	5528	
31111	5529	
31112	5530	
31113	5531	
31116	5534	
31117	5535	
31118	5536	
31120	5538	
31121	5539	
31122	5540	
31123	5541	
31124	5542	
31125	5543	
31126	5544	
31127	5545	
31131	5549	
31132	5550	
31134	5552	
31135	5553	
31136	5554	
31138	5556	
31141	5559	
31142	5560	
31143	5561	
31144	5562	
31145	5563	
31146	5564	
31147	5565	
31149	5567	
31150	5568	
31152	5570	
31154	5572	
31155	5573	
31156	5574	
31158	5576	

31159	5577
31160	5578
31164	5582
31165	5583
31166	5584
31167	5585
31168	5586
31170	5588
31171	5590
31173	5593
31174	5594
31175	5595
31176	5597
31178	5599
31180	5601
31181	5602
31183	5604
31184	5607
31185	5608
31187	5610
31188	5611
31189	5612
31192	5615
31195	5619
31196	5620
31198	5622
31199	5623
31200	5624
31201	5625
31202	5626
31205	5629
31208	5632
31209	5633
31212	5636
31214	5638
31215	5639
31217	5642
31218	5643
31219	5644
31221	5647
31222	5648
31223	5649
31224	5650
31225	5651
31226	5652
31227	5653
31229	5655
31230	5657
31231	5658
31232	5659
31234	5661
31237	5664
31238	5665
31240	5667
31241	5668
31242	5670
31243	5671
31244	5672
31245	5673
31247	5675
31248	5676
31249	5677
31250	5678
31252	5680
31254	5682
31257	5685
31259	5687
31260	5688
31261	5689
31262	5690
31263	5693
31264	5694
31268	5698
31272	5802
31273	5803
31275	5805
31276	5806
31278	5808
31280	5810
31281	5811

31282	5813		
31283	5815		
31284	5816		
31286	5818		
31287	5819		
31288	5820		
31290	5822		
31292	5825		
31293	5826		
31294	5827		
31296	5829		
31298	5831	97203	
31299	5832		
31301	5834		
31302	5835		
31304	5837		
31305	5838		
31306	5839		
31308	5841		
31309	5843		
31311	5845		
31312	5846		
31313	5847		
31314	5848		
31317	5851		
31319	5853		
31320	5854		
31322	5857		
31323	5858		
31324	5859		
31400	31161	5579	
31401	5589		
31402	5592		
31403	5596		
31404	5605		
31405	5606		
31406	5616		
31407	31507	5640	
31408	5646		
31409	5656		
31410	5669		
31411	31511	5691	
31412	31512	5692	
31413	5812		
31415	5824		
31417	5856		
31420	31172	5591	
31421	31140	5558	
31422	31522	31310	5844
31423	31197	5621	
31425	31274	5804	
31426	31526	31193	5617
31427	31194	5618	
31428	31211	5635	
31429	31269	5699	
31432	31153	5571	
31433	31533	31236	5663
31434	31258	5686	
31436	31151	5569	
31437	31537	31182	5603
31439	31239	5666	
31440	31204	5628	
31442	31251	5679	
31443	31177	5598	
31444	31544	31137	5555
31450	31133	5551	
31455	31555	31246	5674
31457	31169	5587	
31460	31266	5696	
31462	31315	5849	
31464	31325	5860	
31467	31216	5641	
31468	31568	31321	5855
31516	31416	5842	
31519	31419	5697	
31524	31424	31157	5575
31531	31431	31253	5681
31541	31441	31220	5645
31545	31445	31300	5833
31546	31446	31316	5850

31547	31447	31295	5828
31548	31448	31148	5566
31549	31449	31307	5840
31551	31451	31318	5852
31553	31453	31114	5532
31556	31456	31291	5823
31558	31458	31303	5836
31569	31469	31277	5807
31602	31191	5614	
31970	97204	31326	5861

Class 33 Type 3 diesel-electric Bo-Bo

33001	6500	
	6502	
33003	6503	
33004	6504	
33005	6505	
33006	6506	
33007	6507	
33009	6509	
33010	6510	
33011	6512	
33013	6518	
33014	6522	
33015	6523	
33016	6524	
33017	6526	
33020	6537	
33022	6540	
33023	6541	
33024	6542	
33026	6544	
33027	6545	
33028	6546	
33031	6549	
33032	6550	
33033	6551	
33034	6552	
33036	6554	
33037	6555	
33038	6556	
33039	6557	
33040	6558	
33041	6559	
33042	6560	
33043	6561	
33044	6562	
33045	6563	
33047	6565	
33049	6567	
33050	6568	
33051	6569	
33054	6572	
33055	6573	
33056	6574	
	6576	
33058	6577	
33059	6578	
33060	6579	
33061	6581	
33062	6582	
33064	6584	
33101	6511	
33104	6516	
33105	6517	
33106	6519	
33107	6520	
33112	6529	
33113	6531	
33114	6532	
33115	83301	6533
33118	6538	
33119	6580	
33203	6588	
33204	6589	
33205	33302	6590
33206	6591	
33209	6594	
33210	6595	
33211	6596	
33212	6597	

Class 35 Type 3 diesel-hydraulic B-B

7000
7001
7002
7003
7004
7005
7006
7007
7008
7009
7010
7011
7012
7013
7014
7015
7016
7019
7020
7021
7022
7023
7024
7025
7026
7027
7028
7030
7031
7032
7033
7034
7035
7036
7037
7038
7039
7040
7041
7042
7043
7044
7045
7046
7047
7048
7049
7050
7051
7052
7053
7054
7055   DB968004
7056
7057
7058
7059
7060
7061
7062
7063
7064
7065
7066
7067
7068
7069
7070
7071
7072
7073
7074
7075
7077
7078
7079
7080
7081
7082
7083
7084
7085
7086
7087
7088
7089   TDB968005
7090
7091
7092
7093
7094
7095
7096
7097
7098
7099
7100

Class 37 Type 3 diesel-electric Co-Co

37004	6704	
37008	37352	6708
37010	6710	
37011	6711	
37012	6712	
37013	6713	
37019	6719	
37026	37320	6726
37031	6731	
37035	6735	
37040	6740	
37043	37354	6743
37045	37355	6745
37046	6746	
37047	6747	
37048	6748	
37051	6751	
37054	6754	
37055	6755	
37058	6758	
37062	6762	
37063	6763	
37065	6765	
37066	6766	
37068	37356	6768
37070	6770	
37071	6771	
37072	6772	
37073	6773	
37074	6774	
37077	6777	
37078	6778	
37079	37357	6779
37080	6780	
37083	6783	
37087	6787	
37088	37323	6788
37092	6792	
37095	6795	
37096	6796	
37098	6798	
37104	6804	
37106	6806	
37107	6807	
37110	6810	
37111	37326	6811
37113	6813	
37114	6814	
37131	6831	
37133	6833	
37137	37312	6837
37138	6838	
37139	6839	
37140	6840	
37141	6841	
37144	6844	
37153	6853	
37154	6854	
37156	37311	6856
37158	6858	

37162	6862		
37174	6874		
37184	6884		
37185	6885		
37191	6891		
37194	6894		
37196	6896		
37197	6897		
37201	6901		
37203	6903		
37209	6909		
37211	6911		
37212	6912		
37213	6913		
37220	6920		
37221	6921		
37222	6922		
37223	6923		
37225	6925		
37229	6929		
37230	6930		
37232	6932		
37235	6935		
37238	6938		
37241	6941		
37242	6942		
37244	6944		
37245	6945		
37251	6951		
37252	6952		
37260	6960		
37262	6962		
37273	37306	6606	
37278	6978		
37280	6980		
	6983		
37293	6993		
37298	6998		
37330	37128	6828	
37331	37202	6902	
37332	37239	6939	
37333	37271	37303	6603
37334	37272	37304	6604
37335	37285	6985	
37341	37015	6715	
37343	37049	37322	6749
37344	37053	6753	
37345	37101	6801	
37351	37002	6702	
37358	37091	6791	
37359	37118	6818	
37370	37127	6827	
37371	37147	6847	
37372	37159	6859*	
37373	37160	6860	
37375	37193	6893	
37376	37199	6899	
37377	37200	6900	
37378	37204	6904	
37379	37226	6926	
37381	37284	6984	
37382	37145	37313	6845
37383	37167	6867	
37384	37258	6958	
37404	37286	6986	
37406	37295	6995	
37408	37289	6989	
37410	37273	6973	
37411	37290	6990	
37412	37301	6601	
37413	37276	6976	
37414	37287	6987	
37415	37277	6977	
37416	37302	6602	
37417	37269	6969	
37420	37297	6997	
37426	37299	6999	
37427	37288	6988	
37428	37281	6981	
37429	37300	6600	

37430	37265	6965
37431	37272	6972
37505	37028	6728
37509	37093	6793
37513	37056	6756
37515	37064	6764
37519	37027	6727
37520	37041	6741
37670	37182	6882
37671	37247	6947
37672	37189	6889
37673	37132	6832
37675	37164	6864
37677	37121	6821
37678	37256	6956
37680	37224	6924
37681	37130	6830
37682	37236	6936
37683	37187	6887
37684	37134	6834
37686	37172	6872
37689	37195	6895
37692	37122	6822
37693	37210	6910
37694	37192	6892
37695	37157	6857
37696	37228	6928
37697	37243	6943
37698	37246	6946
37699	37253	6953
37701	37030	6730
37702	37020	6720
37704	37034	6734
37705	37060	6760
37707	37001	6701
37708	37089	6789
37709	37014	6714
37711	37085	6785
37713	37052	6752
37715	37021	6721
37717	37050	6750
37718	37084	6784
37719	37033	6733
37796	37105	6805
37797	37081	6781
37798	37006	6706
37799	37061	6761
37801	37173	6873
37802	37163	6863
37803	37208	6908
37883	37176	6876
37885	37177	6877
37886	37180	6880
37887	37120	6820
37888	37135	6835
37889	37233	6933
37890	37168	6868
37891	37166	6866
37892	37149	6849
37893	37237	6937
37894	37124	6824
37895	37283	6819
37896	37231	6931
37897	37155	6855
37898	37186	6886
37899	37161	6861
37902	37148	6848
37903	37249	6949
37904	37125	6825

Note: Numbers 37271-274 were used twice
*37372 donated parts of its body to the construction of D5910

Class 40 Type 4 diesel-electric 1Co-Co1

40001	201
40002	202
40003	203
40004	204
40005	205
40006	206

40007	207	
40008	208	
40009	209	
40010	210	
40011	211	
40014	214	
40015	215	
40016	216	
40017	217	
40018	218	
40019	219	
40020	220	
40021	221	
40022	222	
40023	223	
40024	224	
40025	225	
40026	226	
40027	227	
40028	228	
40029	229	
40030	230	
40031	231	
40032	232	
40033	233	
40034	234	
40035	235	
40036	236	
40037	237	
40038	238	
40039	239	
40040	240	
40041	241	
40042	242	
40043	243	
40044	244	
40045	245	
40046	246	
40047	247	
40048	248	
40049	249	
40050	250	
40051	251	
40052	252	
40053	253	
40054	254	
40055	255	
40056	256	
40057	257	
40058	258	
40059	259	
40060	260	97405
40061	261	
40062	262	
40063	263	
40064	264	
40065	265	
40066	266	
40067	267	
40068	268	
40069	269	
40070	270	
40071	271	
40072	272	
40073	273	
40074	274	
40075	275	
40076	276	
40077	277	
40078	278	
40079	279	
40080	280	
40081	281	
40082	282	
40083	283	
40084	284	
40085	285	
40086	286	
40087	287	
40088	288	

40089	289
40090	290
40091	291
40092	292
40093	293
40094	294
40095	295
40096	296
40097	297
40098	298
40099	299
40100	300
40101	301
40102	302
40103	303
40104	304
40105	305
40107	307
40108	308
40109	309
40110	310
40111	311
40112	312
40113	313
40114	314
40115	315
40116	316
40117	317
40119	319
40120	320
40121	321
	322
40123	323
40124	324
40125	325
40126	326
40127	327
40128	328
40129	329
40130	330
40131	331
40132	332
40133	333
40134	334
40136	336
40137	337
40138	338
40139	339
40140	340
40141	341
40142	342
40143	343
40144	344
40146	346
40147	347
40148	348
40149	349
40150	350
40151	351
40152	352
40153	353
40154	354
40155	355
40156	356
40157	357
40158	358
40159	359
40160	360
40161	361
40162	362
40163	363
40164	364
40165	365
40166	366
40167	367
40168	368
40169	369
40170	370
40171	371
40172	372

40173	373
40174	374
40175	375
40176	376
40177	377
40178	378
40179	379
40180	380
40181	381
40182	382
40183	383
40184	384
40185	385
40186	386
40187	387
40188	388
40189	389
40190	390
40191	391
40192	392
40193	393
40194	394
40195	395
40196	396
40197	397
40198	398
40199	399

Class 41 Type 4 diesel-hydraulic A1A-A1A
600
601
602
603
604

Class 42 Type 4 diesel-hydraulic B-B
800
801
802
803
804
805
806
807
808
809
810
811
812
813
814
815
816
817
818
819
820
822
823
824
825
826
827
828
829
830
831
866
867
868
869
870

Class 43 Type 4 diesel-hydraulic B-B
833
834
835
836
837
838
839

840
841
842
843
844
845
846
847
848
849
850
851
852
853
854
855
856
857
858
859
860
861
862
863
864
865

Class 41/43 Type 4 diesel-electric Bo-Bo (HST power car)

41002	43001	ADB975813

Class 43 Type 4 diesel-electric Bo-Bo (HST power car)
43011
43019
43173

Class 44 Type 4 diesel-electric 1Co-Co1

44001	1
44002	2
44003	3
44005	5
44006	6
44007	7
44009	9
44010	10

Class 45 Type 4 diesel-electric 1Co-Co1

45001	13	
45002	29	
45003	133	
45004	77	
45005	79	
45006	89	
45007	119	
45008	90	
45009	37	
45010	112	
45011	12	
45012	108	
45013	20	
45014	137	
45016	16	
45017	23	ADB968024
45018	15	
45019	33	
45020	26	
45021	25	
45022	60	97409
45023	54	
45024	17	
45025	19	
45026	21	
45027	24	
45028	27	
45029	30	97410
45030	31	
45031	36	
45032	38	
45033	39	
45034	42	97411

45035	44	
45036	45	
45037	46	
45038	48	
45039	49	
45040	50	97412
45042	57	
45043	58	
45044	63	
45045	64	
45046	68	
45047	69	
45048	70	
45049	71	
45050	72	
45051	74	
45052	75	
45053	76	
45054	95	
45055	84	
45056	91	
45057	93	
45058	97	
45059	98	
45061	101	
45062	103	
45063	104	
45064	105	
45065	110	
45066	114	97413
45067	115	
45068	118	
45069	121	
45070	122	
45071	125	
45072	127	
45073	129	
45074	131	
45075	132	
45076	134	
45077	136	
45101	96	
45102	51	
45103	116	
45104	59	
45106	106	
45107	43	
45109	85	
45110	73	
45111	65	
45113	80	
45114	94	
45115	81	
45116	47	
45117	35	
45119	34	
45120	107	
45121	18	
45122	11	
45123	52	
45124	28	
45126	32	
45127	87	
45128	113	
45129	111	
45130	117	
45131	124	
45134	126	
45136	88	
45137	56	
45138	92	
45139	109	
45140	102	
45141	82	
45142	83	
45143	62	
45144	55	
45145	128	
45146	66	
45147	41	

45148	130	
45150	45054	78

Note: Number 45054 was used twice

Class 46 Type 4 diesel-electric 1Co-Co1

46001	138
46002	139
46003	140
46004	141
46005	142
46006	143
46007	144
46008	145
46009	146
46011	148
46012	149
46013	150
46014	151
46015	152
46016	153
46017	154
46018	155
46019	156
46020	157
46021	158
46022	159
46023	160
46024	161
46025	162
46026	163
46027	164
46028	165
46029	166
46030	167
46031	168
46032	169
46033	170
46034	171
46036	173
46037	174
46038	175
46039	176
46040	177
46041	178
46042	179
46043	180
46044	181
46046	183
46047	184
46048	185
46049	186
46050	187
46051	188
46052	189
46053	190
46054	191
46055	192
46056	193

Class 47 Type 4 diesel-electric Co-Co

47001	1521
47002	1522
47003	1523
47005	1526
47006	1528
47007	1529
47008	1530
47009	1532
47010	1537
47011	1538
47012	1539
47013	1540
47014	1543
47015	1544
47016	1546
47017	1570
47018	1572
47019	1573
47033	1613
47049	1631
47050	1632

47051	1633	
47052	1634	
47053	1635	
47054	1638	
47063	1647	
47085	1670	
	1671	
47089	1675	
47093	1679	
47094	1680	
47095	1681	
47096	1682	
47097	1684	
47098	1685	
47099	1686	
47100	1687	
47101	1688	
47102	1690	
47103	1691	
47104	1692	
47106	1694	
47107	1695	
47108	1696	
47109	1697	
47110	1698	
47111	1699	
47112	1700	
47113	1701	
47114	1702	
47115	1703	
47116	1704	
47118	1706	
47119	1708	
47120	1709	
47121	1710	
47122	1711	
47123	1712	
47124	1714	
47125	1715	
47130	1721	
47131	1722	
47137	1729	
47140	1732	
	1734	
47142	1735	
47143	1736	
47144	1737	
47145	1738	
47146	1739	
47147	1740	
47148	1741	
47150	47399	1743
47152	47398	1745
47156	1749	
47157	1750	
47159	1752	
47162	1756	
47186	1781	
47188	1838	
47189	1839	
47190	1840	
47191	1841	
47193	1843	
47195	1845	
47196	1846	
47197	1847	
47198	1848	
47199	1849	
47200	1850	
47201	1851	
47202	1852	
47203	1853	
47207	1857	
47208	1858	
47210	1860	
47211	47394	1861
47212	1862	
47213	1863	
47214	1864	
47215	1865	

47217	1867	
47218	1868	
47219	1869	
47220	1870	
47221	1871	
47222	1872	
47223	1873	
47224	1874	
47226	47384	1902
47227	1903	
47228	1904	
47229	1905	
47230	1906	
	1908	
47233	1910	
47235	1912	
47236	1913	
47238	1915	
47241	1918	
47249	1926	
47256	1934	
47258	1938	
47275	1977	
47276	1978	
47277	1979	
47278	1980	
47279	1981	
47280	1982	
47281	1983	
47282	1984	
47283	1985	
47284	1986	
47285	1987	
47286	1988	
47287	1989	
47288	1990	
47289	1991	
47291	1993	
47293	1995	
47294	1996	
47295	1997	
47296	1998	
47297	1999	
47298	1100	
47299	47216	1866
47300	47468	1594
47301	1782	
47302	1783	
47303	47397	1784
47304	47392	1785
47305	1786	
47307	1788	
47308	1789	
47309	47389	1790
47310	1791	
47311	1792	
47312	1793	
47313	1794	
47314	47387	1795
47315	1796	
47316	1797	
47318	1799	
47319	1800	
47320	1801	
47321	1802	
47323	1804	
47324	1805	
47325	1806	
47326	1807	
47327	1808	
47328	47396	1809
47331	1812	
47333	1814	
47334	1815	
47335	1816	
47336	1817	
47338	1819	
47339	1820	
47340	1821	
47341	1822	

47342	1823			47456	1576		
47343	1824			47457	1577		
47344	1825			47458	1578		
47345	1826			47459	1579		
47346	1827			47460	1580		
47348	1829			47461	1581		
47351	1832			47462	1582		
47352	1833			47463	1586		
47353	1834			47464	1587		
47354	1835			47465	1589		
47357	1876			47466	1590		
47358	1877			47467	1593		
47359	1878			47469	1595		
47360	1879			47470	1596		
47361	1880			47471	1598		
47362	1881			47472	97472	1600	
47363	47385	1882		47473	1601		
47365	1884			47474	1602		
47366	1885			47475	1603		
47369	1888			47476	1604		
47370	1889			47477	1607		
47373	1892			47478	1608		
47374	1893			47479	1612		
47377	1896			47481	1627		
47378	47386	1897		47482	1636		
47379	1898			47483	1637		
47380	1899			47485	1683		
47381	1900			47486	1689		
47403	1502			47487	1707		
47404	1503			47489	1716		
47405	1504			47508	1952		
47406	1505			47509	1953		
47407	1506			47512	1958		
47408	1507			47513	1959		
47409	1508			47515	1961		
47410	1509			47518	1101		
47411	1510			47519	1102		
47412	1511			47520	1103		
47413	1512			47521	1104		
47414	1513			47522	1105		
47415	1514			47523	1106		
47416	1515			47525	1108		
47418	1517			47527	1110		
47419	1518			47528	1111		
47420	1519			47529	1551		
47421	1520			47530	1930		
47422	1525			47532	1641		
47423	1527			47533	1651		
47424	1531			47534	1678		
47425	1533			47535	1649		
47426	1534			47536	1655		
47427	1535			47538	1669	ADB968035	
47428	1536			47539	1718		
47429	1541			47540	47975	1723	
47430	1542			47542	1585		
47431	1545			47543	1588		
47432	1547			47544	1592		
47433	1548			47547	1642		
47434	1549			47549	47133	1724	
47435	1550			47550	1731		
47436	1552			47555	47126	1717	
47437	1553			47565	47039	1620	
47438	1554			47566	47043	1624	
47439	1555			47572	47168	1763	
47440	1556			47574	47174	1769	
47441	1557			47575	47175	1770	
47442	1558			47576	47176	1771	
47443	1559			47584	47180	1775	
47444	1560			47624	47087	1673	
47445	1561			47627	47273	1974	
	1562			47628	47078	1663	
47446	1563			47633	47083	1668	
47447	1564			47634	47158	1751	
47448	1565			47645	47075	1659	
47450	1567			47676	47586	47042	1623
47451	1568			47677	47617	47149	1742
47452	1569			47702	47504	1947	
47453	1571			47704	47495	1937	
47454	1574			47706	47494	1936	
47455	1575			47707	47506	1949	

47708	47516	1968		
47709	47499	1942		
47710	47496	1939		
47711	47498	1941		
47713	47510	1954		
47716	47507	1957		
47717	47497	1940		
47721	47557	47024	1591	
47722	47558	47027	1599	
47725	47567	47044	1625	
47726	47568	47045	1626	
47733	47582	47170	1765	
47734	47583	47172	1767	
47736	47587	47263	1963	
47737	47588	47178	1773	
47738	47592	47171	1766	
47741	47597	47026	1597	
47742	47598	47182	1777	
47743	47599	47177	1772	
47745	47603	47267	1967	
47747	47615	47252	1929	
47750	47626	47082	1667	
47756	47644	47246	1923	
47757	47585	47184	1779	
47758	47517	1975		
47759	47559	47028	1605	
47762	47573	47173	1768	
47763	47581	47169	1764	
47764	47630	47041	1622	
47766	47642	47040	1621	
47767	47641	47086	1672	
47774	47801	47551	47153	1746
47775	47531	47974	1584	
47777	47243	47636	1920	
47778	47842	47606	47081	1666
47779	47838	47612	47080	1665
47780	47836	47618	47030	1609
47781	47808	47653	47088	1674
47782	47824	47602	47185	1780
47783	47809	47654	47056	1640
47784	47819	47664	47135	1727
47788	47833	47608	47262	1962
47789	47671	47616	47248	1925
47791	47675	47595	47268	1969
47803	47553	47260	1956	
47829	47619	47264	1964	
47837	47611	47166	1761	
47839	47621	47136	1728	
47844	47556	47020	1583	
47849	47570	47048	1630	
47850	47648	47151	1744	
47852	47646	47074	1658	
47901	47601	47046	1628	
47971	97480	47480	1616	
47972	97545	47545	1646	
47973	97561	47561	47034	1614
47976	47546	1747		
47981	47364	1883		

Class 50 Type 4 diesel-electric Co-Co

50001	401
50003	403
50004	404
50005	405
50006	406
50009	409
50010	410
50011	411
50012	412
50013	413
50014	414
50016	416
50018	418
50020	420
50022	422
50023	423
50024	424
50025	425
50028	428
50032	432
50034	434
50036	436
50037	437
50038	438
50039	439
50040	440
50041	441
50043	443
50045	445
50046	446
50047	447
50048	448

Class 52 Type 4 diesel-hydraulic C-C

1000
1001
1002
1003
1004
1005
1006
1007
1008
1009
1011
1012
1014
1016
1017
1018
1019
1020
1021
1022
1024
1025
1026
1027
1028
1029
1030
1031
1032
1033
1034
1035
1036
1037
1038
1039
1040
1042
1043
1044
1045
1046
1047
1049
1050
1051
1052
1053
1054
1055
1056
1057
1058
1059
1060
1061
1063
1064
1065
1066
1067
1068
1069
1070
1071
1072
1073

Class 53 Type 4 diesel-electric Co-Co

1200	0280

Class 55 Type 5 diesel-electric Co-Co

55001	9001
55003	9003
55004	9004
55005	9005
55006	9006
55007	9007
55008	9008
55010	9010
55011	9011
55012	9012
55013	9013
55014	9014
55017	9017
55018	9018
55020	9020
55021	9021

Class 56 Type 5 diesel-electric Co-Co

56001
56002
56004
56005
56008
56010
56011
56012
56013
56014
56015
56016
56017
56019
56020
56021
56022
56023
56024
56025
56026
56027
56028
56029
56030
56033
56034
56035
56036
56039
56040
56041
56042
56043
56044
56046
56047
56048
56050
56052
56053
56054
56055
56056
56058
56059
56061
56062
56063
56064
56066
56067
56068
56070
56071
56072
56073
56074
56075
56076
56079
56080
56082
56083
56084
56085
56086
56088
56089
56092
56093
56095
56099
56100
56102
56107
56108
56109
56110
56111
56112
56114
56116
56118
56119
56120
56121
56122
56123
56126
56127
56129
56130
56131
56132
56133
56134
56135

Class 58 Type 5 diesel-electric Co-Co

58002
58003
58008
58014
58017
58019
58028
58037
58045

Class 66 Type 5 diesel-electric Co-Co

66521	
66734	66402

Class 70 Type 5 diesel-electric Co-Co

70012

Class 70 750V DC electric Co-Co

20001	CC1
20002	CC2
20003	

Class 71 750V DC electric Bo-Bo

71002	E5002	
71003	E5018	E5003
71004	E5004	
71005	E5020	E5005
71006	E5022	E5006
71007	E5007	
71008	E5008	
71009	E5009	
71010	E5010	
71011	E5011	
71012	E5012	
71013	E5013	
71014	E5014	

Note: Numbers E5003/05/06 were used twice

Class 73 750V DC Electro-diesel Bo-Bo

73004	E6004
73106	E6012
73108	E6014

73111	E6017	
73115	E6021	
	E6027	
73126	E6033	
73131	E6038	
73132	E6039	
73203	73127	E6024

Class 74 750V DC Electro-diesel Bo-Bo

74001	E6101	E5015	
74002	E6102	E5016	
74003	E6103	E5006	
74004	E6104	E5000	E5024
74005	E6105	E5019	
74006	E6106	E5023	
74007	E6107	E5003	
74008	E6108	E5005	
74009	E6109	E5017	
74010	E6110	E5021	

Class 76 1,500V DC electric Bo+Bo

	E26000	6700
76001	E26001	
76002	E26002	
76003	76036	E26036
76004	E26004	
	E26005	
76006	E26006	
76007	E26007	
76008	E26008	
76009	E26009	
76010	E26010	
76011	E26011	
76012	E26012	
76013	E26013	
76014	E26014	
76015	E26015	
76016	E26016	
	E26017	
	E26019	
76021	E26021	
76022	E26022	
76023	E26023	
76024	E26024	
76025	E26025	
76026	E26026	
76027	E26027	
76028	E26028	
76029	E26029	
76030	E26030	
	E26031	
76031	76044	E26044
76032	E26032	
76033	E26033	
76034	E26034	
	E26035	
76035	76018	E26018
76036	76003	E26003
76037	E26037	
76038	76050	E26050
76039	76048	E26048
76040	E26040	
76041	E26041	
	E26042	
76043	E26043	
	E26045	
76046	E26046	
76047	E26047	
76048	76039	E26039
76049	E26049	
76050	76038	E26038
76051	E26051	
76052	E26052	
76053	E26053	
76054	E26054	
76055	E26055	
76056	E26056	
76057	E26057	

Note: Numbers 76003/036/038/039/048/050 were used twice

Class 77 1,500V DC electric Co-Co

	E27005
1503	E27004
1504	E27006
1506	E27002

Class 81 25kV AC electric Bo-Bo

81001	E3001
	E3002
81003	E3004
81004	E3005
81005	E3006
81006	E3007
81007	E3008
	E3009
81008	E3010
81009	E3011
81010	E3012
81011	E3013
81012	E3014
81013	E3015
81014	E3016
81015	E3017
81016	E3018
	E3019
81017	E3020
81018	E3021
81019	E3022
81020	E3023
81021	E3096
81022	E3097

Class 82 25kV AC electric Bo-Bo

	E3046
82001	E3047
82002	E3048
82003	E3049
82004	E3050
82005	E3051
82006	E3052
82007	E3053
	E3055

Class 83 25kV AC electric Bo-Bo

83001	E3024	
83002	E3025	
83003	E3026	
83004	E3027	
83005	E3028	
83006	E3029	
83007	E3030	
83008	E3031	
83009	E3032	
83010	E3033	
83011	E3034	
83013	E3098	E3303
83014	E3099	E3304
83015	E3100	

Class 84 25kV AC electric Bo-Bo

84002	E3037	
84003	E3038	
84004	E3039	
84005	E3040	
84006	E3041	
84007	E3042	
84008	E3043	
84009	E3044	ADB968021
84010	E3045	

Class 85 25kV AC electric Bo-Bo

85001	E3056	
85002	E3057	
85005	E3060	
85008	E3063	
85013	E3068	
85014	E3069	
85015	E3070	
85017	E3072	
85018	E3073	
85019	E3074	
85020	E3075	
85022	E3077	
85023	E3078	
85025	E3080	
85026	E3081	
85027	E3082	
85028	E3083	
85029	E3084	
85030	E3085	
85031	E3086	
85033	E3088	
85034	E3089	
85037	E3092	
85038	E3093	
85039	E3094	
85040	E3095	
85102	85009	E3064
85103	85010	E3065
85104	85012	E3067
85105	85016	E3071
85106	85021	E3076
85107	85024	E3079
85108	85032	E3087
85109	85035	E3090
85110	85036	E3091
85111	85004	E3059
85112	85007	E3062
85113	85003	E3058
85114	85011	E3066

Class 86 25kV AC electric Bo-Bo

86102	86202	E3150		
86103	86203	E3143		
86204	E3173			
86206	E3184			
86207	E3179			
86208	E3141			
86209	E3125			
86211	E3147			
86212	E3151			
86214	E3106			
86216	E3166			
86219	E3196			
86220	E3156			
86221	E3132			
86222	86502	E3131		
86223	E3158			
86224	E3134			
86225	E3164			
86226	E3162			
86227	E3117			
86230	E3168			
86236	E3133			
86237	E3197			
86238	E3116			
86239	86507	E3169		
86240	E3127			
86241	86508	E3121		
86243	E3181			
86244	E3178			
86245	E3182			
86246	86505	E3149		
86247	E3192			
86249	E3161			
86252	E3101			
86254	86047	E3142		
86255	86042	E3154		
86256	86040	E3135		
86257	86043	E3139		
86258	86501	86046	E3140	
86261	86041	E3118		
86416	86316	86016	E3109	
86417	86317	86017	E3146	
86419	86319	86019	E3120	
86425	86325	86025	E3186	
86426	86326	86026	E3195	
86429	86329	86029	E3200	
86430	86030	E3105		
86602	86402	86002	E3170	
86603	86403	86003	E3115	
86606	86406	86006	E3112	
86611	86411	86311	86011	E3171
86615	86415	86315	86015	E3123
86618	86418	86318	86018	E3163
86620	86420	86320	86020	E3114
86621	86421	86321	86021	E3157
86623	86423	86323	86023	E3152
86631	86431	86031	E3188	
86633	86433	86033	E3198	
86634	86434	86034	E3187	
86635	86435	86035	E3124	
86636	86436	86036	E3160	
86901	86253	86044	E3136	
86902	86210	E3190		

Note: Number 86501 was used twice by 86258 and 86608 (the latter still in traffic)

Class 87 25kV AC electric Bo-Bo

87005
87011
87015
87016
87018
87021
87024
87027
87030
87031
87032
87101

Various departmental locos

97020	20
97650	PWM650
97651	PWM651
97652	PWM652
97653	PWM653
97654	PWM654
97701	M61136
97702	M61139
97703	M61182
97704	M61185
97705	M61184
97706	M61189
97707	M61166
97708	M61173
97709	M61172
97710	M61175
ED1	
ED2	
ED3	
ED4	
ED5	
ED6	
ED7	
ED10	
ZM9	

Livery codes

ADZ   Advenza Freight blue
AGA   Abellio Greater Anglia white
AGI   Aggregates industries turquoise and silver
ANG   Anglia Railways turquoise
ATW   Arriva Trains Wales turquoise, unbranded
AVD   AV Dawson red
BAF   Bardon Aggregates blue with Freightliner branding
BBM   Battle of Britain Memorial Flight graphics
BDB   Boston Docks blue
BIF   Biffa red bodyside, orange cabs (GBRf)
BLE   Unspecified plain blue
BLK   British Railways black
BLL   British Rail 'large logo' blue with yellow cabs
BLU   British Rail blue yellow cabsides
BMT   Bulmarket red
BRB   British Rail blue with full yellow ends
BRE   British Rail Blue with large numbers and emblems
BRF   British Rail blue with Union flags
BRL   British Rail blue large logo blue with black roof
BRP   British Rail blue grey prototype HST
BRW   British Rail blue with wasp stripes
BRY   British Railways blue with Foster Yeoman branding
BRZ   BZK BR blue
BYP   British Rail blue with small yellow panels
BZK   BZK (Българска Жеиезолътна Компания) green and yellow
CAL   Caledonian Sleeper blue
CAS   Castle Cement light grey
CCE   Civil engineers' grey/yellow 'Dutch'
CCT   Civil engineers' grey/yellow 'Dutch' with Transrail logos
CEL   Celsa black with orange cab
CEM   Cemex white and blue
CFD   Chemins de fer Départméntaux orange
CMX   Cemex white (GBRf)
COL   Colas Rail Freight orange, yellow and black

CON   Continental rail blue
COR   Corus silver
COT   BZK Cotswold Rail silver
COU   Colas Rail Freight orange, yellow and black unbranded
COY   Corus yellow
CRS   Chiltern Railways silver/grey
CSM   Continental Railway Solution maroon
DBC   DB Cargo red
DBM   DB Cargo Manager's Train silver
DBR   Deutsche Bahn all over red
DBS   DB Schenker red
DBU   DB red unbranded
DCG   Devon & Cornwall Railways green
DCN   DC Rail revised light grey
DCR   DC Rail grey
DEP   Departmental grey
DGB   BZK DRS blue with orange cab
DNS   Nederlandse Spoorwegen grey/yellow
DRA   Drax silver
DRC   DRS blue with Compass logos
DRE   DRS blue with new Compass logos (Class 88)
DRN   DRS blue with new Compass logos
DRS   DRS blue original
DRU   DRS blue, unbranded
DRX   DRS blue with smaller Compass logos
DST   Deanside Transit lilac
EBY   Electric blue yellow panels
ECR   Euro Cargo Rail light grey
EMB   East Midlands Trains blue
EMY   GBRf with Emily Woodman graphics
EPX   Europhoenix silver
ETF   Eurovia Travaux Ferroviaires yellow
EUE   Eurostar grey with EWS logos
EUK   Eurostar grey
EWS   EWS maroon and gold
EWR   EWS maroon and gold with RSS logos
FER   Fertis grey
FEU   Fertis grey unbranded
FGA   First Great Western blue with advertising wrap
FGB   First Great Western blue
FGO   Fragonset black unbranded
FGU   First Great Western blue unbranded

FGS	First Great Western 'special' graphics	LAM	Lamco orange
FLG	Freightliner two tone grey	LHO	Loadhaul original
FLR	Freightliner green with yellow cabs	LNE	Virgin Red with LNER branding
FLY	Floyd black	LNR	BZK LNWR blackberry black
FPG	Freightliner green unbranded	LNW	LNWR grey
FPH	Freightliner 'Powerhaul' green, yellow and grey	LON	London Midland black and green
		LOR	Loram advertising graphics
FRG	Fragonset black	LSW	LSWR black
FSR	First ScotRail blue	LUB	GBRf London Transport Museum black with graphics
FTF	Fall the Fallen graphics		
GBF	GB Railfreight blue and orange	LUW	GBRf London Transport Museum white with graphics
GBR	GB Railfreight blue and orange Europorte style		
		MAA	DB Cargo with WH Malcolm graphics
GBO	GB Railfreight blue and orange original style	MAL	WH Malcolm, green, yellow and blue
		MAR	Lakeside & Haverthwaite Railway lined maroon
GBZ	GB Railfreight blue and orange with minor variations		
		MEW	Mainline Freight blue with EWS logos
GCR	Grand Central black	MFY	Maroon with full yellow ends
GFY	British Railways green full yellow ends	MID	Midland Railway maroon
GLA	Glaxo chemicals blue and dark grey	MLB	Mainline Freight blue
GOP	Golden Ochre with yellow panels	MRM	Metropolitan Railway maroon
GNY	British Railways green no yellow ends	MRT	GBRf Maritime blue
GRE	Unspecified plain green	MSC	GBRf with Medite Sorrento graphics
GWO	Genesee & Wyoming orange and black	MWS	Maroon with wasp stripes
GWS	British Rail green with wasp stripes	MYP	Maroon with yellow panels
GWT	Great Western Trains all over green	NBU	Northern Belle umber and cream unbranded
GWR	Great Western Railway green		
GYP	British Railways green with yellow panels	NCB	National Coal Board blue
		NOB	Northern Belle umber and cream
HAN	Hanson aggregates blue and silver	NOR	Northern purple
HAR	'Harry Patch' black graphics	NRA	National Railway Museum advertising wrap
HNO	Harry Needle Railroad Company orange		
HOP	Hope Construction white with purple solebar	NRB	National Railway Museum light blue
		NRM	National Railway Museum maroon
HST	Original blue, grey, yellow HST	NRY	Network Rail yellow
HUN	Hunslet green	NSD	Network SouthEast revised darker blue
ICM	BR InterCity 'Mainline'	NSE	BZK Network SouthEast red white and blue
ICO	BR InterCity original style		
ICS	BR InterCity Swallow style	NSO	Network SouthEast original with white window frames
IGX	BR InterCity Gatwick Express		
IOS	BR InterCity original with ScotRail branding	NSR	Network SouthEast revised with blue window frames
IND	Industrial livery	OXB	Oxford blue
JUB	DB Cargo Diamond Jubilee silver	POW	Powder blue
JFU	Jarvis Fastline unbranded grey	PUL	Pullman umber and cream
KBR	Knorr Bremse green, white and blue	RCA	Railcare red white and blue
LAB	'Laira' blue with grey roof	RCG	Railcare grey and white

RED	Unspecified plain red
REG	Regional Railways blue and grey
RES	Rail Express systems red and dark grey
REW	Railfreight Distribution 'European' two tone grey with EWS logos
RFD	Railfreight Distribution two tone grey with RfD logos
RFE	Railfreight Distribution 'European' two tone grey with RfD logos
RFO	Railfreight Original grey
RFS	RFS grey
RMB	RMS Locotec black
RMS	RMS Locotec blue
ROG	Rail Operations Group blue
ROY	Royal Scotsman plum
RSR	Railfreight Red stripe
RTC	Railway Technical Centre red and blue
RTO	Royal Train plum
RTP	Royal Train Res style
SCR	ScotRail Saltire blue
SCT	ScotRail HST
SIL	Silverlink green, purple and white
SOU	Southern green and white
SPE	Bombardier special purple, green, blue and red
STO	Stobart Rail advertising
SWU	South West Trains blue unbranded

TAB	Tata Blue
TAS	Tata Silver
TEW	Trainload grey with EWS logos
TLA	Trainload grey with Aggregates logos
TLC	Trainload grey with Coal logos
TLH	Trainload grey with Loadhaul logos
TLM	Trainload grey with Metals logos
TMF	Trainload grey with Mainline Freight logo
TMT	Transmart Trains green
TTG	Two tone unbranded Railfreight grey
TRA	Transagent black and blue
TRB	Transagent red, black and white
TRN	Transrail grey
TSO	TSO yellow
UKR	UK Rail Leasing grey with yellow cabs
UND	Undercoat/unpainted/primer
VEA	Virgin Trains red with advertising branding
VEC	Virgin Trains East Coast With LNER Branding
VFS	Virgin Trains Flying Scotsman
VIR	Virgin Trains red
WCR	West Coast Railways maroon with yellow panels
XCT	CrossCountry Trains

Pool codes

ATLO	Alstom Traincare Locomotives
ATZZ	Alstom Traincare Locomotives For Disposal
AWCA	West Coast Railway Operational Diesel Locomotives
AWCX	West Coast Railway Stored Diesel Locomotives
BREL	Boden Rail Engineering
CDJD	Central Services/Serco Railtest Ex Serco Shunters
CFOL	Class 50 Operations Ltd
CFSL	Class 40 Stored Locos
COFS	Colas Rail Freight
COLO	Colas Rail Freight Hire Locomotives
COLS	Colas Rail Freight Stored Locomotives
COTS	Colas Rail Freight Locomotives For Refurbishing
DBLX	Deltic Preservation Society
DDIN	Freightliner Shunter Fleet
DFGH	Freightliner Heavy Haul
DFGI	Freightliner Intermodal
DFHG	Freightliner Heavy Haul
DFHH	Freightliner Heavy Haul
DFHJ	Freightliner Heavy Haul RHTT/Limited Use
DFIM	Freightliner Intermodal Modified
DFIN	Freightliner Intermodal Low Emission
DFLC	Freightliner Intermodal
DFLH	Freightliner Heavy Haul
DFNC	Freightliner Awaiting Maintenance
DHLT	Freightliner Stored/Not In Main Line Use Locomotives
EFOO	First Great Western FGW Class 57/6
EFPC	First Great Western FGW Class 43
EFSH	First Great Western FGW Shunters
EHPC	Arriva CrossCountry HST Power Cars
EJLO	London Midland Shunters
ELRD	East Lancashire Railway Operational Locomotives
EMPC	East Midlands Trains HST Power Cars
EMSL	East Midlands Trains Shunters
EPEX	Europhoenix For Scrap/Export
EPUK	Europhoenix UK Locomotives
GBBR	GBRf Class 73/9 – Brush Repowered
GBBT	GBRf UK Cab – Long Range Fuel Tanks
GBCH	GBRf Caledonian Sleeper

GBCS	GBRf Re-Engineered
GBEB	GBRf Euro Cab – Long Range Fuel Tanks
GBED	GBRf Electro Diesel Locos For Hire
GBEE	GBRf On Hire Class 20
GBEL	GBRf Euro Cab – Standard Fuel Tanks
GBET	GBRf Stored Locos
GBFM	GBRf RETB Fitted Locomotives
GBHN	GBRf Long Term Hire Locomotives
GBLT	GBRf UK Cab – Standard Fuel Tanks
GBNB	GBRf New Build Locos
GBNR	GBRf For Network Rail Use
GBRT	GBRf Restricted Locos
GBSL	GBRf Caledonian Sleepers
GBST	GBRf Caledonian Sleepers/Channel Tunnel
GBWM	GBRf Shunting Duties
GBYH	GBRf General Pool
GCHP	Grand Central HST Power Cars
GPSS	Eurostar UK Operate From TI (DBC Maintained)
GROG	Rail Operations Group Operational Locos
HAPC	ScotRail Class 43
HBSH	Virgin Trains East Coast On Hire To VTEC
HISE	Rail Vehicle Engineering East Midlands Trains Shunters
HTLX	Hanson Traction Operational Locomotives
HYWD	South West Trains Thunderbird Locos
IANA	Greater Anglia Loco Fleet
IECA	Virgin Trains East Coast Operational Locomotives
IECP	Virgin Trains East Coast HST power cars
KDSD	Bombardier Doncaster
MBDL	Non TOC Private Owner – Diesel locos
MBED	Non TOC Private Owner – Class 73
MBEL	Non TOC Private Owner – Electric locos
MOLO	RT Rail Limited Hired Fleet Shunter locos
MRLO	RMS Locotec Ex-FM Rail Operational Locos
MRLS	RMS Locotec Ex-FM Rail Stored locos

MRSO	RMS Locotec Ex-FM Rail Operational Shunters	WQAA	DB Cargo UK Locomotives Stopped Serviceable – Group 1A
NRLO	Nemesis Rail Locomotives On Hire	WQAB	DB Cargo UK Stored Locomotives Group 1B
NRLS	Nemesis Rail Ex-FM Rail Stored locos		
QACL	Network Rail Load Bank	WQBA	DB Cargo UK Stored Locomotives Stored Serviceable – Group 2
QADD	Network Rail Diesel Locos		
QCAR	Network Rail HST Power Cars	WQCA	DB Cargo UK Stored Locos For Component Recovery – Group 3
QETS	Network Rail European Signalling		
RCZH	Knorr Bremse Rail Systems Springburn Works Shunters	WQDA	DB Cargo UK Stored Locomotives Surplus – Group 4
		XHAC	Direct Rail Services Operational Locos – ETS Equipped
RCZN	Knorr Bremse Rail Systems Wolverton Works Shunters		
RFSH	Wabtec Rail Locomotives	XHCC	Direct Rail Services Operational Locos – Northern (Cumbrian Coast Workings)
RMSX	RMS Locotec Locomotives		
RTSO	Riviera Trains Operational Shunters		
RVLO	Railway Vehicle Engineering Derby Operational Locomotives	XHCE	Direct Rail Services Hire To Chiltern Railways
		XHCK	Direct Rail Services Operational Locos
SAXL	Eversholt Rail Off Lease Locos	XHIM	Direct Rail Services Intermodal Locos
SBXL	Porterbrook Leasing Off Lease Locos	XHNC	Direct Rail Services Nuclear Traffic
SCXL	Angel Train Contracts Off Lease Locos	XHSS	Direct Rail Services Stored Locos
TTLS	Traditional Traction/Railway Support Services	XHTP	Direct Rail Services Locos For Transpennine Express
		XHVE	Direct Rail Services Vossloh Locos
UKRL	UK Rail Leasing On Lease	XHVT	Direct Rail Services West Coast Thunderbird Locos
UMRM	UK Rail Leasing Not Main Line		
UKRS	UK Rail Leasing Stored	XYPA	Mendip Rail Operational Locomotives
WAAC	DB Cargo UK	XYPO	Mendip Rail Operational Locomotives
WABC	DB Cargo UK RETB Fitted		
WAWC	DB Cargo UK Arriva Wales Hire		
WBAE	DB Cargo UK Fitted With Stop/Start Technology		
WBAR	DB Cargo UK Remote Condition Monitoring Equipment		
WBAT	DB Cargo UK General		
WBBE	DB Cargo UK RETB & Stop/Start Technology Fitted		
WBBT	DB Cargo UK RETB Fitted		
WBLE	DB Cargo UK Lickey Bankers With Stop/Start Technology		
WBLT	DB Cargo UK		
WBTT	DB Cargo UK RHTT – Tripcock Fitted		
WCAT	DB Cargo UK Standard Fuel Range		
WCBT	DB Cargo UK Extended Fuel Rail		
WDAM	DB Cargo UK		
WEAC	DB Cargo UK		
WFBC	DB Cargo UK HS1 Equipped		
WGEA	DB Cargo UK Euro Cargo Rail		
WGEE	DB Cargo UK Eastern Europe		
WGEP	DB Cargo UK Poland		

Depot codes

AB	Albacete, Spain Continental Rail	CL	Crewe LNWR
AC	Alicante, Spain Transfesa	CM	Cambridge Arriva CrossCountry
AH	Asfordby Technical Centre Network Rail	CO	Coquelles, France Eurotunnel
AN	Allerton Alstom	CQ	Crewe Railway Age Trust
AT	Attercliffe European Metal Recycling	CP	Crewe Carriage Shed Arriva
AZ	Alizay, Nr. Rouen, France DB Cargo	CR	Crewe Gresty Bridge Direct Rail Services
BB	Billingham Sembcorp Utilities	CS	Carnforth West Coast Railways
BD	Boston Docks Victoria Group	CZ	Burton Central Rivers Bombardier
BH	Barrow Hill Roundhouse	DC	Craiova Romania exported locos
BK	Bristol Barton Hill LNWR	DD	DB Cargo Daventry International Railfreight
BL	Loughborough Falcon Works Wabtec/Bruch Traction		Terminal Malcolm Rail
BM	Bournemouth West South Western Railway	DF	Derby RTC Loram (UK)
BN	Bounds Green Virgin Trains East Coast	DG	Dagenham
BO	Bo'ness Scottish Railway Preservation Society	DK	Konkar Bulgaria exported locos DB Cargo
BQ	Bury East Lancs Railway	DL	Dean Lane Manchester
BS	Bescot DB Cargo	DM	Dollands Moor Eurotunnel
BU	Burton-on-Trent Nemesis Rail	DS	Deanside Deanside Transit
BZ	Sofia, Bulgaria BZK Българска Жеиезолътна Компания	DY	Derby Etches Park East Midlands Trains
CA	Castle Donington storage site	EC	Craigentinny Virgin Trains East Coast
CB	Crewe Basford Hall Network Rail	EG	Liverpool Edge Hill Alstom
CC	Cardiff Steelworks Celsa	EK	Shepherdswell East Kent Railway
CD	Crewe DMD Locomotive Services Limited	EH	Eastleigh DB Cargo
CE	Crewe International Electric DB Cargo	EY	Ely Potter Group Logistics
CF	Cardiff Canton Colas Rail Freight	FD	Mobile Maintenance, Mainline Diesels Freightliner
		FE	Mobile Maintenance, Mainline Electrics Freightliner

FG	Garston Ford		LR	Leicester UK Rail Leasing
FP	Mobile Maintenance, Poland Freightliner		LW	Longtown (Smalmstown) MoD
FS	Mobile Maintenance, Diesel Shunters Freightliner		MA	Manchester International Traincare Alstom
FT	Fréthun, France DB Cargo		MB	Middlesbrough AV Dawson
FX	Felixstowe Freightliner		MD	Merehead Aggregated Industries
GO	Grosmont North Yorkshire Moors Railway		MG	Margam DB Cargo
HA	Haymarket ScotRail		MQ	Machen Quarry Hanson Aggregates
HH	Hams Hall Associated British Ports		NC	Norwich Crown Point Abellio Greater Anglia
HO	Hope Hope Construction		NL	Neville Hill East Midlands Trains
HQ	Headquarters		OO	Old Oak Common HST Great Western Railway
HT	Newcastle Heaton Northern/Grand Central		OY	Oxley Alstom
HUN	Hungary Floyd		PD	Teesport PD Ports
IN	UK Industrial Sites		PG	Peterborough GB Railfreight
IS	Inverness ScotRail		PM	Bristol St. Philip's Marsh Great Western Railway
KM	Carlisle Kingmoor Direct Rail Services		PN	Rybnik/Poznan, Poland DB Cargo
KR	Kidderminster Severn Valley Railway		PO	Polmadie Alstom
KT	Ketton Cement Works Heidelburg Cement Group		PU	Immingham Puma Energy
KY	Knottingley DB Cargo		PZ	Penzance Great Western Railway
LA	Plymouth Laira Great Western Railway		RR	Doncaster Roberts Road EMD/GB Railfreight
LD	Leeds Midland Road Freightliner		RU	Rugby Rail Plant Colas Rail Freight
LE	Swansea Landore Great Western Railway		SB	Shrewsbury Coleham Yard Network Rail
LG	Manchester Longsight Electric Alstom		SC	Scunthorpe Steelworks Tata Steel
LH	Barton-under-Needwood LH Group Services (Wabtec)		SE	St. Leonards St Leonards Engineering
LM	Long Marston Quiton Rail		SH	Southall Railway Centre West Coast Railways
LO	Manchester Longsight Diesel Alstom			

SI	Soho
	London Midland
SK	Swanwick
	Midland Railway Butterley
SL	Stewarts Lane
	Southern
SM	Southampton Maritime
	Freightliner
SP	Wigan Springs Branch
	DB Cargo
SS	Shotton Steelworks
	Tata Steel
TC	Toton Training Compound
	DB Cargo
TI	Temple Mills International
	Eurostar
TM	Tyseley Locomotive Works
	Vintage Trains
TO	Toton
	DB Cargo
TR	Trostre Steelworks
	Tata Steel
TS	Tyseley
	London Midland
TX	Thuxton
	Mid Norfolk Railway
TY	Toton Yard
	DB Cargo
WB	Wembley Traincare
	Alstom
WC	Washwood Heath
	Cemex
WD	Widnes
	Alstom
WG	Whitemoor Yard
	GB Railfreight
WH	Washwood Heath
	Boden Rail Engineering/DC Rail
WI	Wishaw
	Moveright International
WN	Willesden
	GBRf/LOROL

WO	Wolsingham
	Weardale Railway
WP	Woippy, France
	DB Cargo
WQ	Headquarters
WR	Leeming Bar
	Wensleydale Railway
WY	Westbury Yard
	DB Cargo
WZ	Warsaw, Poland
	Freightliner
YK	York
	National Railway Museum
ZA	Derby RTC Business Park
	Loram
ZB	Doncaster Works
	Wabtec
ZC	Crewe Works
	Bombardier Transportation
ZD	Derby Litchurch Lane Works
	Bombardier Transportation
ZG	Eastleigh Works
	Arlington Fleet Group
ZH	Glasgow Springburn, Works
	Knorr Bremse Rail Systems
ZI	Ilford Level 5 Works
	Bombardier Transportation
ZK	Kilmarnock Works
	Wabtec
ZN	Wolverton Works
	Knorr Bremse Rail Systems
ZO	Kingsbury
	European Metal Recycling
ZR	Rotherham
	CF Booth Ltd
ZS	Wakefield
	RMS Locotec
ZW	Stoke-on-Trent Works
	Axiom Rail/Turners/Marcroft

Owner codes

ACL	AC Locomotive Group	GBR	GB Railfreight
AGI	Aggregates Industries	GWR	Great Western Railway
AGO	Andrew Goodman	HAN	Hanson Aggregates
ALS	Alstom	HJE	Howard Johnston
ANG	Angel Trains	HNR	Harry Needle Railroad Company
ARV	Arriva Group	LES	Les Ross
BEA	Beacon Rail	LOL	London Overground
BEN	Steve Beniston	LOM	Lombard Finance
BOD	Neil Boden	LON	London Midland
CFA	Class 50 Alliance	LSL	Locomotive Services Limited
CFP	Class 40 Preservation Society	MAQ	Macquarie Group
CFS	Class 56 Group	MOW	Michael Owen
COL	Colas Rail Freight	NEM	Nemesis Rail
CTL	Class 20 Locomotive Society	NET	Network Rail
DBC	DB Cargo	NRM	National Railway Museum
DCR	DC Rail	POR	Porterbrook
DPS	Deltic Preservation Society	ROG	Rail Operations Group
DRS	Direct Rail Services	SFG	Stratford Class 47 Group
DTG	Diesel Traction Group	SOA	71A Locomotives
EEG	English Electric Group	SRP	Scottish Railway Preservation Society
EMT	East Midlands Trains	STG	Scottish Class 37 Group
EPX	Europhoenix	SW	Shaun Wright
EUK	Eurostar	TRA	Transagent (Croatia)
EVS	Eversholt Leasing	UKR	UK Rail Leasing
FIR	First Group	VIN	Vintage Trains
FLI	Freightliner	WCR	West Coast Railways
GAR	Garcia Hanson		

Spot hire/industrial owners

AFS	Arlington Fleet Services	LAM	Lamco Mining
AVD	AV Dawson	LOR	Loram
BOM	Bombardier	NYM	North Yorkshire Moors Railway
BMT	Bulmarket (Bulgaria)	RSS	Railway Support Services (Traditional Traction)
BZK	BZK (Българска Жеиезолътна Компания, Bulgaria)	SEC	Serco
CON	Continental Rail Solutions (Hungary)	SLE	St Leonards Engineering
CRB	Chris Beet	TFA	Transfesa
EMD	Electromotive Diesels	TMT	Transmart Trains
EMR	European Metal Recycling	TLW	Tyseley Locomotive Works
FLY	Floyd (Hungary)	VIC	Victoria Group (Boston Docks)
ITY	Private owner in Italy	WAB	Wabtec
KBR	Knorr Bremse		

Heritage railway locations

ALL   Allely's yard, Studley
ALN   Aln Valley Railway
AVR   Avon Valley Railway
BAT   Battlefield Line
BH   Barrow Hill Roundhouse
BKR   Bo'ness & Kinneil Railway
BIR   Barry Island Railway
BLU   Bluebell Railway
BRC   Buckingham Railway Centre
BWR   Bodmin & Wenford Railway
BU   Burton on Trent
CAL   Caledonian Railway
CHR   Chasewater Railway
CHV   Churnet Valley Railway
CPR   Chinnor & Princes Risborough Railway
CRT   Cambrian Railways Trust
CWR   Cholsey & Wallingford Railway
CVR   Colne Valley Railway
DFR   Dean Forest Railway
DAR   Dartmoor Railway
DRC   Didcot Railway Centre
DVR   Derwent Valley Light Railway
EBR   Embsay Steam Railway
EDR   Eden Valley Railway
EKR   East Kent Railway
ELR   East Lancashire Railway
EOR   Epping and Ongar Railway
ESR   East Somerset Railway
EVR   Ecclesbourne Valley Railway
FHR   Fawley Hill Railway
GWR   Gloucestershire Warwickshire Railway
GCR   Great Central Railway

GCN   Great Central Railway Nottingham
GIR   Gwili Railway
IWR   Isle of Wight Steam Railway
KWV   Keighley & Worth Valley Railway
KES   Kent & East Sussex Railway
LHR   Lakeside & Haverthwaite Railway
LLR   Llangollen Railway
LWR   Lincolnshire Wolds Railway
MAL   Private site Malton
MHR   Mid Hants Railway
MNR   Mid Norfolk Railway
MOL   Moreton-on-Lugg
MRB   Midland Railway, Butterley
MRM   Mangapps Railway Museum
NRM   National Railway Museum York
NRS   National Railway Museum Shildon
NLR   Northampton and Lamport Railway
NNR   North Norfolk Railway
NVR   Nene Valley Railway
NYM   North Yorkshire Moors Railway
NTR   North Tyneside Railway
PBR   Pontypool & Blaenavon Railway
PDR   Paignton & Dartmouth Railway
PKR   Peak Rail
PVR   Plym Valley Railway
RAC   Railway Age Crewe
RDR   Royal Deeside Railway
RHR   Rushden Heritage Railway
RSR   Ribble Steam Railway
RVR   Rother Valley Railway

SCR   Swindon & Cricklade Railway
SDR   South Devon Railway
SPA   Spa Valley Railway
STM   Stainmoor Railway
STR   Strathspey Railway
SWR   Swanage Railway
SVR   Severn Valley Railway
TBR   Trawsfynydd & Blaenau Railway
TIT   Titley Junction
TSR   Telford Steam Railway
VBR   Vale of Berkeley Railway
WH   Washwood Heath
WIS   Wishaw
WEN   Weardale Railway
WEA   Wensleydale Railway
WSR   West Somerset Railway